ʟɪᴛᴇʀᴀᴛᴜʀᴇ & ʜᴏᴜɢʜᴛ

Decisions, Decisions

Perfection Learning

EDITORIAL DIRECTOR	Julie A. Schumacher
SENIOR EDITOR	Terry Ofner
EDITOR	Rebecca Christian
PERMISSIONS	Laura Pieper
REVIEWERS	Mary Gershon
	Lynne Albright
	Ann Tharnish

DESIGN AND PHOTO RESEARCH

Jan Michalson
Lisa Lorimor
Karen Bump
Sue Cornelison

COVER ART BYZANTINE ISOMETRIC 1951 Ben Shahn
© Estate of Ben Shahn/Licensed by VAGA, New York, NY

ACKNOWLEDGMENTS

"Ashes" by Susan Beth Pfeffer, from *Places I Never Meant To Be: Original Stories* by Censored Writers, edited by Judy Blume. Copyright © 1999 by Susan Beth Pfeffer. Reprinted by permission of the author.

"Button, Button" by Richard Matheson. Originally published in *Playboy*, May 1970. Copyright © 1970 by HMH Publishing Co., renewed 1998 by Richard Matheson. Reprinted by permission of Don Congdon Associates, Inc.

"Certain Choices" from *Selected Poems, 1969 - 1981*, by Richard Shelton, copyright © 1982. Reprinted by permission of the University of Pittsburgh Press and the author.

"The Dandelion Garden" by Budge Wilson, from *The Dandelion Garden and Other Stories*, copyright © 1995 by Budge Wilson (American edition). Canadian edition entitled *Cordelia Clark*, copyright © 1994 by Budge Wilson. Used by permission of Philomel Books, a division of Penguin Putnam, Inc., and Stoddart Publishing Co. Limited (Canada). CONTINUED ON PAGE 143

How Do I Make a Decision?

The question above is the *essential question* that you will consider as you read this book. The literature, activities, and organization of the book will lead you to think critically about this question and to develop a deeper understanding of how to make wise decisions.

To help you shape your answer to the broad essential question, you will read and respond to four sections, or clusters. Each cluster addresses a specific question and thinking skill.

CLUSTER ONE   What influences a decision? **ANALYZE**

CLUSTER TWO   Good decision or bad decision? **EVALUATE**

CLUSTER THREE   What are the possible consequences of our decisions? **PREDICT**

CLUSTER FOUR   Thinking on your own **SYNTHESIZE**

Notice that the final cluster asks you to think independently about your answer to the essential question—*How do I make a decision?*

Decisions, Decisions

The Road Not Taken

Two roads diverged in a yellow wood,
And sorry I could not travel both
And be one traveler, long I stood
And looked down one as far as I could
To where it bent in the undergrowth;

Then took the other, as just as fair,
And having perhaps the better claim,
Because it was grassy and wanted wear;
Though as for that, the passing there
Had worn them really about the same,

And both that morning equally lay
In leaves no step had trodden black.
Oh, I kept the first for another day!
Yet knowing how way leads on to way,
I doubted if I should ever come back.

I shall be telling this with a sigh
Somewhere ages and ages hence:
Two roads diverged in a wood, and I—

I took the one less traveled by,
And that has made all the difference.

Robert Frost

Table of Contents

Thinking Skill   SYNTHESIZING

"Prisoner's Dilemma"

The Decision Game

Picture yourself a spy, one of several operating undercover in a totalitarian nation. One day, you and a fellow spy are caught by the authorities. Your captors keep you in separate rooms and question you individually.

The sentence for spying in this country is life imprisonment under terrible conditions. But the official who is questioning you offers you a deal. If you inform on the other captured spy—and if the other captured spy does *not* inform on you—then you can go free, and the other spy will remain in prison for life.

The very idea of informing on a colleague offends your sense of honor. "I'll never inform," you reply angrily. "Do your worst."

Your questioner smiles grimly. "An admirable choice," he says. "And indeed, if both you and your colleague remain silent, we don't have enough evidence to give you the usual life sentences. The longest would be ten years."

"Ten years it is, then," you say stubbornly—and with just a trace of relief. Ten years is much better than life, after all.

Then your questioner bends toward you menacingly. "Before you make a final decision," he says, "consider that your colleague is in the room next door with another questioner. And your colleague is being offered exactly the same deal."

You feel a swell of alarm. Does your colleague have the same sense of honor that you do? How tempted might he or she be by an offer of freedom at the price of informing on *you?* If you remain silent and your colleague informs, then your colleague will go free—and you will spend the rest of your life in prison!

Suddenly, your choice does not seem so simple. What do you decide?

A well-known game called the Prisoner's Dilemma is based on such a situation. If both prisoners inform (or "defect") each receives only one point. If both prisoners keep silent (or "cooperate") each receives three points. If one prisoner defects and the other cooperates, the defecting prisoner receives five points, while the cooperating prisoner is left with zero. The game becomes much more interesting (and more nerve-racking!) if played out repeatedly.

The game of Prisoner's Dilemma raises disturbing questions about decision making—questions that recur in the selections throughout this book. For example, how do we make decisions when we can't predict their outcomes? And how do we balance self- interest against loyalty to others?

To be sure, few of us will ever find ourselves in situations as dire as that of the prisoner in the game. We make countless decisions daily which are fairly simple and clear-cut—how much to study for a test, perhaps, or how to dress on a cold winter day. But sooner or later, we also find ourselves in more troublesome situations.

For example, what do you do when you know that a friend is involved in some illegal activity? Or when a lie will get you out of trouble? Or when loyalty to an unpopular friend means sacrificing your own popularity? Some dilemmas have no easy answers. Those dilemmas—and how we deal with them—offer a true test of who we are.

CAGE 1981 Magdalena Abakanowicz

CONCEPT VOCABULARY

You will find the following terms and definitions useful as you read and discuss the selections in this book.

agonize to worry about making a decision

ambivalence a feeling of being torn between two choices

default to refuse to make a decision or to postpone doing so until other forces intervene and determine the outcome

crux an essential point requiring resolution of a problem (for example, "The crux of the matter was whether to stay at the party where others were using drugs, or to leave and risk losing friendships.")

deliberate to think about and discuss issues and decisions carefully

destiny what a person receives in life as distributed by fate or chance (for example, "It was her destiny to be born rich.")

ethics a system of values and morals

fate a force that determines outcomes and endings regardless of what individuals do; similar to destiny. (for example, "Fate cut their travels short in the form of a blizzard.")

free will voluntary choice or decision

inevitable incapable of being avoided

intuition a hunch or gut feeling

irrevocable not possible to take back or revoke

morals feelings and judgments about right and wrong that guide a person's behavior

priority something that deserves more attention than competing alternatives (for example, "He wanted to make a phone call, but his paper route was his first priority.")

quandary a state of doubt (for example, "She was in a quandary over which college to attend.")

rationalize to attribute actions to good motives without acknowledging the real and deeper reasons (for example, "She rationalized cheating on the test because her parents pressured her to get good grades.")

relent to bend or give in

superstition a belief in magic or chance

waver to go back and forth between opinions or choices; to fluctuate

CLUSTER ONE

What Influences a Decision?
Thinking Skill ANALYZING

Playing God

OUIDA SEBESTYEN

He was almost to the river, walking fast, when he saw Laurel on her bicycle, racing to catch him. In a space between the gusts of raw March wind she yelled, "Josh, wait up, or I'll break your legs."

So he wasn't going to get away without saying good-bye after all.

Laurel came puffing up, fierce and wind-whipped. He braced himself as she stared at the duffel bag he'd taken from his folks' closet and stuffed with all the clothes and things he thought he'd need.

"You're doing it," she said. The pain that came into her eyes hurt him, too. "Why? Without telling me? I thought we were friends! If I hadn't seen you sneaking through the alley—"

We *are* friends, he wanted to assure her. Best friends. The best. But he said, walking on, "So? One more thing I didn't do right today." Suddenly it came pouring out. "At breakfast they jumped down my throat about my grades. Then they got started on why can't I grow up and shape up and do my part now with him out of work. Boy. I didn't get him laid off."

"But it's a hard time for them, Josh."

"Not for her. She's tickled pink. All this schooling's going to get her back into that *career* she gave up when I came along." It seemed vital to stay cold and angry. Even with Laurel. Especially with Laurel, because she knew what he really was. "So I figured I've been enough trouble—I might as well get on out there and do something with my life." He stared at the distant river waiting to be crossed.

"It's dumb," Laurel said, with the directness they had never been afraid to use with each other. "They'll just haul you back. Parents aren't perfect. You're feeling sorry for yourself." She stopped in the road, trying to make him turn around, rethink. But he kept walking. "Please, Josh," she said behind him. "Don't do it."

"You're leaving," he said.

"But not until school's out. And I wouldn't be, if we didn't have to move out to the Coast."

"But you are," he said. It wasn't her fault, he knew. She couldn't make her own choices. But he could. "Maybe I'll see you in sunny Cal."

"How'll you live, without money?" she asked into the wind. "Josh? How'll you eat? It scares me."

He turned around. She was outlined against the far-off knob of land called Throne of Kings, where they had sat one day in dusty autumn grass, growing quieter and quieter until their faces turned and their mouths touched in a kiss as intent and sunstruck as the silent hawks gliding over them.

His feet kept moving him backward. "Hey, just don't worry about me," he called. "Nobody else does. Okay?" She didn't answer, but her eyelids blinked fast. He relented. "Would you come as far as the bridge with me?"

She shook her head. "I have to get back to the library. I'm supposed to be helping with the party right now."

Hearing her say she should be getting punch and cookies ready for some stumpy old lady who wrote bad poetry, at the moment he was running away, gave him the new rush of anger he needed to turn around and march out of her life.

The river sprawled ahead of him, more sand than water. There was an eeriness in what he was doing: leaving someone he cared so much about without ending it right. He wished she'd run after him. But what could she say?

When he got to the bridge he looked back, expecting to see her pedaling away, but she stood in the road, her hair blowing across her funny freckled face.

The long bridge turned his footsteps hollow as he started across. He had planned to wait for the bus at the crossroad a mile or so farther on. Between wind gusts he found himself straining to hear the hum of traffic. But the only sound was closer, a small lonesome squeak like a bird he didn't recognize, or something grating under the bridge.

When would they notice he'd left home? he wondered. Maybe they wouldn't even miss him.

Near the end of the bridge the sound got louder. He scanned the sky and the flat brown horizon. Then he leaned over the bridge rail and looked down into a cardboard box on the sand at the water's edge. A jumble of yips and squeals came from something dark squirming inside it.

He felt his muscles clamp into knots. He had to catch a bus. He was this far. He had to straighten up and walk on past whatever was down there crying for help. But he couldn't.

He glanced at Laurel. She hadn't moved. He went to the far end of the bridge and climbed down through the weeds. The box twitched as he bent warily and looked in.

Puppies. Five of them, no bigger than fuzzy mittens, crawling in their prison.

Josh drew a weary sigh and squatted to touch them. They went silent, rooting hungrily against his hands. He lifted up a soft black puppy with eyes that melted a hole in his heart, and dropped it back into the pile. "No," he warned them. "I can't do anything, you guys. No."

Their little claws grated on the high sides of the box as they struggled to reach him. He saw Laurel hanging over the bridge rail. "What's down there, Josh?" she called.

"Five puppies," he called back.

She came scrambling down. Her eyes were blazing. "What kind of gut-less wonder would throw them into the river! Oh, look at them." She gathered two against her cheeks.

"Maybe somebody couldn't take care of them," he said, trying to be fair. But it wasn't fair. He flicked his hands angrily, staying aloof. "Didn't want to be bothered. So, plop, off the bridge."

"But it's cruel," she said. "It's sad. Like back in early times, in the book Miss Rainey gave you, remember? When people left the defective babies on a mountain so if the gods wanted them saved they could do a miracle." Suddenly she handed him a puppy. "And guess what—along came good old Josh."

"No," he said. "Dang—I've got a bus to catch!" He dropped the puppy into the heap, as trapped as it was. "Why me? What'll I do with the dumb things?"

"You said you've always wanted a dog. You just got five of your wishes." She looked at his eyes and stopped trying to make him smile.

"Take them back into town and find them homes. There'll be another bus. If you still . . . "

He followed her gaze down the road he should be striding along, and turned helplessly to the box. "Want a nice puppy?"

"Oh, I do. But my mom's deathly allergic. And when we move I couldn't take it—we'll be renting till we find a house." She nudged him up onto the bridge. "Stand in front of the supermarket, Josh. Won't you? Somebody'll take them. Look, I've got to get back, or I'll get canned."

She went to her bike, but her worried eyes kept studying him. He could feel the box pressing against the folded lump of bus-ticket money in his pocket. What did she want? Why should he be the one to care, when nobody else did?

"Do you think they'd fall out of my basket if I tried to carry them?" she asked.

"You just worry about getting on back," he said. Her face fell. It touched him to see how hard she was trying to keep this from being good-bye. He shrugged, defeated. "They're not all that heavy. But you could carry the duffel."

▲ ▲ ▲

Most of the shoppers glanced into his box and went on past to buy their groceries. A few paused. The children stopped and stayed, cuddling puppies until they were dragged away by their parents.

He felt stupid. He resented what those helpless crawling blobs in the box had done to his plans, and was still angry at the person who had left them by the edge of the river. And at himself because he hadn't.

Several times, during the hour he stood in front of the store, he saw a shadowy movement at one of the high library windows down the block. Laurel. Checking to see what luck he was having. Or if he had left.

He felt exposed, there in full view of everyone on the street. He knew that his mother was thirty miles away, in one of those nifty workshops that was going to expand her options. But his dad might drive past any minute, checking out a job prospect, and see him and the duffel. He couldn't take a public quarrel, not after leaving that morning feeling so righteous and ready.

A little girl forced her mother to stop at the box.

"Could I have one?" she begged, entranced.

"They'd make great pets. Or watchdogs, or whatever," Josh said quickly, trying to cover every possibility.

The woman smiled. "How much?"

"Oh, free," Josh exclaimed. "Free. And they don't eat much at all."

The woman squeezed the little girl, almost laughing. "Which one do you like?"

The little girl picked up each puppy in turn, studying it nose to nose. The last one stretched to give her a lick. "This one," she breathed, dazzled. "He likes me already!" She turned suddenly to Josh. "We'll love it good."

"We will," the woman agreed. "Thank you."

He felt an unexpected emptiness as they walked away huddled over their treasure. He guessed it was for the puppy leaving the warmth of its brothers and sisters forever, with its little head jiggling trustfully. Or maybe it was because the woman hugged the little girl the way his father hugged him in his fantasies.

A man came out of the store. Proud of his change of luck, Josh had opened his mouth to say, "How about a beautiful puppy?" when he noticed that the tag on the man's jacket said MANAGER.

He gathered up his duffel and his dogs, and mushed.[1]

As he passed the library, Laurel leaped out onto the top step and beckoned. "Josh! I saved some cookies for you."

He climbed up, weary. "A lady took a puppy."

Her glad smile faded. "You've only given away *one?*"

"Miss Rainey won't like me bringing them into the library, either," he said. "Have you started the party for old lady Snap Crackle Pop?"

Laurel nodded. "Grace Whipple Cox," she corrected him. "She's sitting

---

1 **mushed:** moved out quickly. ("Mush" is a command used to tell sled dogs to pull harder.)

there, waiting to autograph a stack of books taller than she is, that nobody wants to buy."

He went in, trying to be invisible behind Laurel. A tiny, round powder keg of a lady in a velvet hat sat talking to a few matronly types[2] holding punch cups and paper napkins. He could see now why Laurel called her the Gnome de Plume,[3] although at first she'd had to explain the pun to him. He was curious about anybody who could write poetry. He'd tried it himself. Nobody knew, except Laurel, unless Miss Rainey had guessed.

Laurel led him to a little room full of magazines and gave him four pink cookies. "What'll you do now?" she asked. "Oh, Josh, they're hungry. When they're this young they need food every few hours. Could I give them some coffee-creamer stuff, do you think?"

"I don't know. Maybe not." Yips began to come from the box. He put his jacket over it. "I've got to give them *away*. This is crazy."

"Let's try Miss Rainey," Laurel said. "I know she has cats, but maybe—" She winced as the yapping rose in a needle-sharp chorus.

He started through the door with his box and almost bulldozed Miss Rainey off her feet as she started in.

"What on earth!" She flipped through her memory card index for his name. "Josh. What have you got?" She looked in. Her face softened. "Well bless their little deafening hearts."

"Somebody left them under the bridge," Laurel said.

Miss Rainey breathed an angry sigh.

"I found a home for one already." Josh tilted the box so Miss Rainey would see yearning eyes and smell warm puppy. "Laurel thought maybe you'd like one."

"Oh, listen, Josh, they're already trying to zone my house as a zoo. I just couldn't. I'm gone all day. Cats and chameleons and macaws can manage. But a puppy—nope." She turned away. Then she gestured him close again, and muttered, "Try the literary ladies. It's a long shot, but try."

She was leading them out through rows of shelves, when she stopped abruptly. Every face they saw was staring at a long table of refreshments. Another of Miss Rainey's assistants, a little older than Laurel, sat at a punch bowl with her mouth ajar. Her startled eyes were riveted on a scruffy man with no socks who was helping himself to punch and cook-

---

2 **matronly types:** older married women

3 **Gnome de Plume:** a reference to the poet, who looks like a gnome—a short, dwarflike creature. Gnome de Plume is a play on the French phrase *nom de plume,* meaning "pen name."

ies. His hand, the size of a baseball mitt, was already stacked with sand tarts and brownies and macaroons[4] and six of those pink cartwheels Josh had wolfed down in the little room. The man drained his paper cup, smiled at the hypnotized girl, and refilled it. He studied his hand, and added another brownie.

Miss Rainey came alive. "Good lord—he's cleaning us out! Where did he come from?" She headed toward the man so vigorously that Josh thought she was going to grab his cookies. But she drew herself tall and said, "Sir, have you met our distinguished guest, or read her previous books of poetry?"

The scraggy man froze in his tracks. "I can't say I have," he admitted, still chewing. "But I did literally cut my teeth on poetry, ma'am. The complete unexpurgated[5] works of Rudyard Kipling, if I remember rightly." He gave her a big shameless smile, then studied the puppies in Josh's box. "Part shepherd, wouldn't you say—the ears and head shape?"

He left Miss Rainey speechless and walked into the reference section to finish his meal in peace. The girl at the punch bowl exclaimed in a whisper, "I didn't know what to *do,* Miss Rainey! When he started loading up—"

Miss Rainey patted her shoulder mechanically. "It's all right." Her face had softened as it had when she saw the puppies. "He's hungry."

Laurel elbowed Josh toward the autographing table. A boy from high school was interviewing the Gnome de Plume, scribbling frantically at half the speed of her rushing words. Josh stopped at a distance, not wanting to interrupt but eager to get the women's attention when he could. Somebody had to take another puppy.

"Could you explain why you entitled your newest book *The Second Highest Point in Beymer Country*?" the boy asked.

"To make a statement," the Gnome de Plume snapped, from behind the stack of unsold books. "Everybody knows that Crown Hill is the highest point—it's on the maps, it's written about. We act as if second-best is second-rate. I wanted to say that there can be only one topmost *anything*—all the rest of this glorious fascinating world is second. Or third, or tenth. Empty words. Hogwash. Everything has worth, for its own reasons." She knocked the mountain of books askew.[6] "I'm not even a

---

4 **macaroons:** coconut cookies

5 **unexpurgated:** uncut

6 **askew:** out of order

tenth-rate poet, although you don't have to quote me on that. I'm just a funny old lady. But why shouldn't I write a *ton* of poetry if I want to? God doesn't label blades of grass Grade A and Grade B. He creates. For the fun of it! Because he's a creator!"

The boy had lost her, back at Crown Hill. Josh watched him write down GRADE A and take a bite of his pencil.

Two of the literary ladies, equally startled, peeped into Josh's box. Miss Rainey said, "Listen, we need homes for these abandoned little things. Someone dropped them in the river without having the decency, or the heart, to finish the job."

The ladies shook their heads sadly. One said, "A ten-to-fifteen-year commitment is too much for me. Besides, they need children to play with. A farm or something." They turned away from the box, unobtrusively[7] putting distance also between themselves and the old lady glaring around her mountain of books.

"What's the second highest point in Beymer County?" Josh whispered.

A pink flush crossed Laurel's face. "Throne of Kings," she whispered back.

He felt his own cheeks go warm. There would never be a spot on earth higher than the Throne of Kings on an autumn day, enchanted by hawks. *Why do you have to leave me?* he wanted to beg her through the ache in his throat.

But he was leaving first. You do it to them before they do it to you. You don't just stand there on the reject pile, smiling like it doesn't hurt.

The grungy guy tapped him on the shoulder. "You say you're giving pups away?" His cookies were gone, except for the frosting on his beard.

Josh nodded, surprised.

"I'll take one," the man said.

Everyone looked at Josh. The man put his paper cup on the stack of books. It looked like a lighthouse.

"Oh," Miss Rainey said. "I don't think—" She stopped, flustered.

"I don't know," Josh said carefully. "I mean—I don't know you." He hadn't known the woman with the little girl, either, he remembered. "Aren't you just—on the road? I mean, if you don't have a job or anything, how could you feed it, and all?"

"I live here," the man said. "Hey, I wouldn't take it if I couldn't come up with the goods. I take care of *me*, don't I? What's your name? I look

---

7 **unobtrusively:** subtly; quietly

like I can manage to take care of a pup, don't I?"

"Josh," he told him, nodding in spite of his doubts.

"Joshua fit the battle of Jericho,"⁸ the man said, as if he had the habit of telling himself things. "Well, Josh, you trust me or you don't. It's a risk."

"I don't know," Josh said in desperation. How could he tell? What kind of life would a puppy have with a man like that?

But what did it take to beat dying in a box by the river?

Suddenly the man grubbed in the pocket of his ragged pea jacket⁹ and brought out a pencil in a handful of lint and crumbs. "I'll tell you what, Josh, my friend, I'll give you my address. You come check on me. Check on your pup—see if I don't do a commendable¹⁰ job on it." He handed Josh a napkin with a street number on it. There were no houses there, Josh knew from his paper route days. A warehouse. So? Guard dogs stayed in warehouses okay. The man gave him a half glance with wary watery eyes. He's begging, Josh thought. It's rough by yourself.

He held out the box. "Which one do you want?"

The man said softly, "The runt." He lifted out the smallest puppy, smoothing its fuzzy head with his thumb. He said, "You keep that address. You come out and check."

"I will," Josh warned him. "You better be telling me the truth."

The man tucked the puppy inside his jacket. "I'll be gentle with it, Josh, my friend. I had a belt taken to me too many times to ever lift my hand to another creature."

He bowed to the ladies, smiling, and went out.

The Gnome de Plume thrust a book into Laurel's hand. "Run catch him," she ordered. Her squinty old eyes glinted with what looked to Josh like pleasure.

Laurel darted out. Josh felt a spurt of happiness. Two pups down—three to go. The rest of March, April, May before Laurel left. They'd go to the Throne of Kings again, and this time he would be able to say, *I'm glad we knew each other and liked and loved each other. Even if it can't be the way I wanted it to be.*

The Gnome de Plume brought a box from under the table and began to fill it with her books. The ladies gathered to help.

---

8 **Joshua fit the battle of Jericho:** a reference to Joshua in the Bible, who fought a battle against the odds; it is also the first line of a well-known spiritual

9 **pea jacket:** a short, double-breasted coat, usually navy blue

10 **commendable:** admirable; worthy

Josh was folding the napkin into his pocket when his hand froze. What was he doing? He wasn't going to be here to check on anybody's address. He was going to be out there on a bus. Finding his own warehouse to sleep in. There wouldn't be another day on the Throne of Kings. Never another day. He slung his head, blinking as if he'd run into a door in the dark.

He went out blindly and stood on the sidewalk, breathing hard. The box of puppies, lighter now, bulged and bumped in his hands. Laurel came back and stood beside him. They watched the cars go by in the long afternoon shadows.

"Were you just saying that?" she asked, with a pinched, anxious smile. "When you told him you'd check on the puppy?"

A car like his dad's came toward them. He went tight. It passed, driven by a boy in a baseball cap. Josh let out his breath. His voice, sounding far away, said, "Just once, if my folks would just look up and notice I was there. That's all it would take."

Laurel nodded. She always nodded, understanding, and he always went on explaining and defending himself, like some kind of neglected machine grinding itself to pieces.

"I mean, they talk to me—sure—but they're doing other things while they're yelling at me. Like I was some emergency they wished they weren't having."

Grace Whipple Cox came out the door with a load of books. Miss Rainey followed with another box and the last of the cookies under plastic on a wobbly paper plate.

"Let me carry that," Laurel said, taking the Gnome's load. Josh set the puppies down and took the books and plate from Miss Rainey. They followed the Gnome down the chilly street to her beat-up car and put the boxes in the back.

"Not much of an afternoon, dollar-wise," she said. He didn't understand why she followed them back to the library. She looked down at the puppies. "I wish I was sure I *had* ten-to-fifteen years to commit," she said, and laughed. "But so what? We can't wait for life to be perfect, can we?" She lifted up two puppies.

He heard Laurel draw a soft breath.

The Gnome de Plume said, "I can't take all three—I'm tempting fate as it is. But fate has sent them a guardian angel once already." She smiled at Josh. "Fate can do it again, if I don't last long enough. And they'll have each other." She bent closer. "Would you like one of my books?"

He gulped. "Yes," he told her, taking it. "I would."

The Gnome smiled at Laurel and handed her the puppies. "Come, young lady. I'll drive you home."

Laurel turned to Josh. Her anxious eyes tried to read his. "Your duffel is in the little room."

"I know," he said. He didn't move.

Slowly she started after the Gnome. "Josh?" she entreated, looking back.

"It won't work," he said. "I go home—they're madder than ever—we start yelling—"

"Part of that's up to you, isn't it?" she asked.

Her soft words let him down with a thump. Dang—*help* me, he wanted to yell. Don't just pile it back on me.

"Josh, can't you try? We have to get through things the best we can." Her voice was shaking. "I'll listen and listen, if it'll help, but it's up to you, finally."

He turned away. Inside the library he stared through the window as the Gnome's car, and then others, and then others, passed in the dusk.

▲ ▲ ▲

His dad was watching the news. He asked, "Where've you been?" without turning from the TV.

Josh felt the eeriness start again, matching the jumpy light of the screen that lit the room. He took the puppy out of his jacket. It seemed like fate, really, because the one that had been left was the one whose tender eyes had grabbed his heart beside the river.

"What's that?" his dad said, when he noticed. "You can't keep a dog. Your mother's got too much to do already."

"She won't have to take care of it," Josh said, keeping his voice even and slow. "I will. Feeding and housebreaking and shots and tags and spaying and everything."

His dad looked at him a long time. "Talk is cheap," he said.

"I guess you're going to have to risk it," Josh said, braced against the gaze.

His dad turned back to the news. "She can't do everything. The house, her schooling. She's got big dreams for herself. Give her a chance."

The puppy tried to crawl inside Josh's collar. He had to feed it. He had to buy a bag of something. "I live here too," he said. He felt for his ticket money. Maybe if he called Laurel she'd walk to the store with him and carry the pup while he lugged home a bag of dog chow. And they could talk. "Give me a chance too. Okay?"

His dad switched channels uneasily, testing, rejecting. He doesn't know how to answer me, Josh thought. He doesn't know what to say to any of this—to not having a job, or to her getting ahead of him, or to being my father.

A commercial came on. His dad said, watching it, "When I went into the army my folks kept my dog for me. They said he got lost. Ran away. But I was never sure." His face slowly warped[11] in the shifting light. "Maybe he tried to find me. Or maybe he got killed and they hated to tell me. So I never could be sure, you know? For a long time I used to listen to the dogs barking, off in town. For years, I guess. Hoping I'd hear him."

Josh stopped halfway to the door. Hesitantly he came back, and sat on the arm of the couch, stroking the hungry puppy with his thumb. He stared at the television like his dad, not seeing it. Even with the sound turned high, he caught himself trying to hear other things. The far-off whine of buses. The almost inaudible cries and urgings and answers coming from everywhere. ∾

---

11 **warped:** twisted; bent out of shape

Dusting

JULIA ALVAREZ

Each morning I wrote my name
on the dusty cabinet, then crossed
the dining table in script, scrawled
in capitals on the backs of chairs,
practicing signatures like scales
while Mother followed, squirting
linseed from a burping can
into a crumpled-up flannel.

She erased my fingerprints
from the bookshelf and rocker,
polished mirrors on the desk
scribbled with my alphabets.
My name was swallowed in the towel with
    which she jeweled the table tops.
The grain surfaced in the oak
and the pine grew luminous.
But I refused with every mark
to be like her, anonymous.

TLA

JANE McFANN

I trudged down the hallway of Yannick High School, my nearly empty backpack bumping painfully against my still-sore spine. I should have felt light—happy, or at least relieved, but I didn't. I felt heavy, as if the effort required to lift one foot after another was more than should be asked of me. I thought I heard footsteps behind me, not quite footsteps but more like echoes of footsteps just slightly out of rhythm with my own. I turned to look down the long hallway, half expecting to see the math teacher whose classroom I had just left.

There was no one there.

Somehow I wasn't surprised. I walked out of the building, glad to escape the stale air. There's something almost eerie about a silent school long after the school day has ended, emptied of the shouting, thudding bodies. As usual my hand trembled as I searched through my book bag for the keys to the still-unfamiliar car my parents had insisted on buying for me.

"If you don't drive again now, you'll never be able to do it," they reasoned. I knew they were right, but that never stopped the trembling.

I tossed my book bag across the seat and slid behind the wheel. The bag was empty of its normal burden of textbooks. I'd turned them all in today, including the math one. Math had been the last test left to make up. All of my teachers had complimented me on my diligence in making up the two months' worth of work that I had missed. I should have been pleased. All that was left now was the graduation ceremony itself, five days from now.

I knew I should have been excited. Ever since I'd been a little girl, I'd dreamed about walking across the stage in cap and gown, wearing the yellow sash that designates an honors graduate.

At least my parents would be happy.

The book bag contained nothing but my filled-up notebooks and folders stuffed with old papers. Unused to its lightness, it slid off the seat and onto the floor of the passenger's side. I heard the thud of the one book it still contained, and I began to tremble harder.

I thought that I was going home to the bed I went to each day, a welcome destination for my back and my head and my leg that still ached fiercely. I refused to take the painkillers the doctor had given me. Somehow the pain seemed necessary.

I didn't go home. One turn after another after another, the car seemed guided in the opposite direction. I knew where I was going, even though I didn't want to go there.

I pulled the car onto the shoulder of the road, a remote turnoff that few had reason to discover. The road led to an area that once was a rock quarry but now was abandoned, leaving a sharp, tall cliff alongside the river. I could hear the rumbling of the small waterfall a few hundred yards downstream.

"There should be a guardrail here," I had said to Jake the first time he brought me here.

"Why?" he asked. "Anybody who chooses to come here should be able to see the risk." He stepped closer to the edge. We were only fourteen then, and we had ridden our bicycles for miles to get there on a hot August afternoon. I could still see him as he was then—legs slender in worn jeans, T-shirt stuck to sweaty chest. The muscles would come a few years later when he discovered soccer and wrestling and that skinny body filled out.

I grabbed his arm and pulled him back from the edge.

"What?" he asked.

"You scare me that close to the edge," I said.

"Come here and look down," he said.

"No," I answered, trying to keep him back.

"Come here," he said. "It's beautiful. Trust me. I'll hold on to you. I won't let you fall."

I trusted Jake. I always had, ever since we met when we were ten years old. I let him take me to the edge. I didn't see the beauty that he saw when he looked down to the jagged rocks and rushing water, but I saw why it fascinated him. There was a power there, a ruthlessness that pulled him closer, and me with him. He locked his arms around me, and we stared into the water.

"Would you die if you fell?" I finally asked, my voice a whisper.

"Probably," he said. "If the rocks didn't get you, the waterfall would." There was no fear in his voice, but rather respect.

When he held me that day, I knew we'd never be childhood buddies again.

Everyone said they could never imagine us apart, probably because we so rarely were. HollyandJake—one word. My girlfriends envied me because I always had a boyfriend, always had a date to the movies or the prom or the game.

Except this year's prom of course.

HollyandJake. Every vision I ever had of my future included Jake. Even my parents had never told me to date others or complained that I was too young to get serious. In fact there were times when I accused them of loving him more than they loved me.

The only major argument Jake and I had, they sided with him. I got offered a scholarship at a school seven hundred miles away, and when I showed the letter to Jake, he screamed at me.

"How can you even consider taking that?"

"Jake, it's nice to be offered something like this."

"You mean you'd leave me? I can't believe you even applied there." Jake had no desire to go to college. His father owned a large farm, and all Jake had ever wanted to do was to work the land. He could make anything grow, calm any animal, accept any force of nature.

"I'll never leave you," I said. There was a certainty in me that I never would, a certainty mixed with just a touch of another feeling I couldn't quite identify.

Maybe sadness.

Maybe security.

I wrote the letter turning down the scholarship that same night. After all, the local university was good too.

"He's just a little insecure," my mother explained. "He's afraid that when you have a college degree and he doesn't, you'll outgrow him."

"I'll never outgrow him," I said, "but he can't stop me from growing in my own way."

"He knows that," my mother said. "He's just afraid."

"Jake's never afraid," I said. He was so sure of himself, so knowing about what he wanted.

A piece of land of his own.

Me.

Near the edge of the cliff there is a tree. Not just any tree. My tree. It is a holly tree that soars at least forty feet into the air. Jake and I visited it in every season: in the spring when the new growth sprouts delicate and green, in summer when flocks of birds visit its prickly protection, in winter when red berries glow against the icy white of the snow.

"I can't believe it wasn't torn down by the quarrying," I said to Jake when we first noticed it.

"It was meant to be here for you," Jake said.

On my sixteenth birthday Jake took me there. He gave me a small box, carefully wrapped. I expected jewelry. What I got was a Swiss Army knife.

Jake must have seen the surprise on my face. "Wait. Let me explain," he said. He took me under the wide branches of the holly tree and pointed to a smooth place on the trunk. "There. Right there," he said.

I understood. I opened the largest blade on the knife, and carefully, painstakingly carved a heart into the trunk of the holly tree. Inside the heart I carved:

Holly

and

Jake

TLA

True Love Always.

In the next years that's what Jake would murmur to me at the end of a long, sleepy, late-night telephone conversation. That's what he would whisper after our last kiss.

I ducked under the branches of the holly tree, hauling my book bag with me, and traced the heart and the letters over and over again with my fingers.

TLA.

I sat on the ground, sweeping away the prickly leaves, and finally, trembling so badly that I could barely work the zipper, I opened my book bag and took out the one remaining book.

I'd only gotten the book that morning. I ran my fingers over the red, rough-textured cover with the smooth gold embossed seal of the school.

I didn't want to open it, but I had to. It was a new pain to be faced, a pain that I had to endure, deserved to endure.

TLA.

I opened the cover of the yearbook and paged through it methodically. Page after page brought images of Jake.

Soccer team.

In a crowd shot of a pep fest.

Leaning against a doorway, smiling that slightly crooked smile of his.

He and I in the Senior Superlatives section: Senior-Class Couple.

Jake by himself: Best Looking.

Me by myself: Most Likely to Succeed.

HollyandJake, holding hands in the hallway.

People didn't envy me much these days. In fact they didn't even talk to me much. I knew it was because they didn't know what to say. I knew it was because they were afraid of saying the wrong thing. I knew it was because I wasn't exactly a sparkling conversationalist myself these days.

"She's still in a lot of pain," I heard them whisper in the hallway.

"It just doesn't seem right to see Holly without . . ."

And then there was the other whisper I heard at night when I stared into the darkness.

TLA.

And the footsteps that I heard behind me in quiet hallways when there was nobody there.

TLA.

"Jake would want you to go on with your life," my mother said. "He would want you to be happy."

"Don't ever leave me," I heard him whisper, with a refrain that sounded like wind blowing through a holly tree or distant water flowing over rocks.

My fingers traced his senior picture in the yearbook. I never liked it that much. He looked uncomfortable in a coat and tie, and there was no sign of that slightly crooked smile that had helped me grow up. When I thought of Jake, I saw him in old jeans worn thin and nearly white at the knees and a red plaid flannel shirt, his hands dirty, his face aglow.

"Look, Holly. The first flowers are open on the honeysuckle. Isn't that the sweetest smell in the world? Come here, Holly. Smell the honeysuckle."

And I would smell the honeysuckle, and I would smell the healthy, earthy, sweaty smell of Jake, and I could not tell which was sweeter.

I shivered despite the warmth of early June, and I shut the yearbook. The pain in my back intensified, but I refused to shift my position.

"Why won't you take the pain medicine?" my mother recently asked, the pain in her eyes mirroring the pain in mine. "You don't have to punish yourself. You know it wasn't your fault. You *do* know that, don't you?"

That's what the police told me. The car that hit us was driven by an old man who had had a heart attack and veered wildly into our lane, not giving me a moment to react. I'd had my seat belt on, and I'd awakened in the hospital with no memory of the accident except the back and head and leg injuries.

"Jake?" I said as soon as I regained consciousness. "Jake?"

"Take it easy," my mother said, and a nurse immediately stuck a needle in my arm. I was sure, as I slipped into darkness, that Jake was beside me, holding my hand.

"Jake," I murmured drowsily the next time I awoke.

"Holly, there's something you need to know," my mother said.

"No," I said, knowing what she was going to say. "He's here with me."

That was the first time I heard the whisper.

TLA.

I sat under the holly tree and picked up some of the leaves, closing my fingers over them, deliberately letting the sharp points puncture my skin.

If I hadn't wanted to go to that party . . .

If I hadn't insisted on driving . . . Jake was a better driver than me. Maybe he could have swerved.

If I had made him put on his seat belt. That was the big one. I'd fussed at him before about that, but he always said a seat belt kept him too far away from me.

"Never leave me. Promise you'll never leave me."

Doctors claim that the will to live is important. I got better anyway. My body, young and strong, healed, leaving only the pain behind.

"You're lucky not to have any scars," one girl said. After she saw the look on my face, she, too, stopped talking to me.

I slowly rose off the ground beneath the holly tree. I thought I was going to the car, but I wasn't. I walked to the edge of the drop-off and looked down. The water rushed busily over the jagged rocks; the waterfall made the water thrash a few hundred yards downstream.

TLA, came the whisper. It could have been the wind or the water, but it wasn't.

I looked over the edge, curiously unafraid. I put down my book bag, its notebooks and folders a part of life as far away as childhood.

TLA.

I held the yearbook in both hands, feeling its weight, watching the filtered afternoon sun glint off the gold of the school emblem.

TLA, came the whisper. *Don't ever leave me.*

I held out the yearbook and opened my hands, watching it fall. It fell swiftly and gracefully, no fluttering pages, no hesitation. It hit once on the jagged gray rocks and then was swept away by the water.

Don't ever leave me, came the whisper.

I knew what I was supposed to do. I knew it as deeply and as certainly as I knew that Jake loved me.

"No," I said. "Let me grow in my own way."

TLA, came the whisper.

TLA.

What future could ever be complete or happy without Jake? How could I spend the rest of my life with half a heart, half a soul, and no slightly crooked smile to guide me?

Trust me, said the whisper.

I always had.

"Are you sure?" I said, my voice quiet but calm.

TLA, came the answer.

I leaned over the water, trying to give myself to the whisper. I leaned until my muscles screamed in agony. I willed myself to let go.

In the last second before I let go, I smelled something very familiar. It was honeysuckle, and mixed with it was a strong, earthy, sweaty smell.

"No, Jake," I said, pulling back a step. "I have to stay for a while longer. I have to smell the honeysuckle. I have to grow a little more. For you. And for me."

Never leave me, said the whisper, fading softer and softer, lost in the slightest touch of the breeze.

"I won't," I said. "As long as there is honeysuckle, I'll never leave you." ❧

President Richard Nixon resigning from office, 1974

"I would have preferred to carry through"

RICHARD M. NIXON

When President Richard Nixon was faced with almost certain impeachment, he became the first U.S. president to resign from office. Nixon was the 37th president, from 1969 until 1974, when the Watergate burglary and its cover-up developed into a scandal that toppled his presidency in the second year of his second term.

The Watergate scandal began on June 17, 1972, when five men with ties to the Republican Nixon Administration were surprised while searching through the office of the rival Democratic National Committee, located in the Watergate Hotel in Washington, D.C. It was never fully established what the men were looking for, though they were wearing surgical gloves, their pockets were stuffed with $100 bills, and they were rifling through files, photographing some of them. They were also attempting to repair a telephone bug that had been installed three weeks before.

Nixon initially denied his administration's involvement, but audio tapes of his conversations with his staff proved otherwise. Ultimately, 25 men associated with the burglary and cover-up landed in prison. When a grand jury named Nixon a coconspirator, he resigned from the presidency. He was later pardoned by Gerald Ford, his former vice-president and successor in office. The following is an excerpt from his resignation speech.

. . . In all the decisions I have made in my public life, I have always tried to do what was best for the Nation. Throughout the long and difficult period of Watergate, I have felt it was my duty to preserve, to make every possible effort to complete the term of office to which you elected me.

In the past few days, however, it has become evident to me that I no longer have a strong enough political base in the Congress to justify continuing that effort. As long as there was such a base, I felt strongly that it was necessary to see the constitutional process through to its conclusion, that to do otherwise would be unfaithful to the spirit of that deliberately difficult process and a dangerously destabilizing[1] precedent for the future.

But with the disappearance of that base, I now believe that the constitutional purpose has been served, and there is no longer a need for the process to be prolonged.

I would have preferred to carry through to the finish, whatever the personal agony it would have involved, and my family unanimously urged me to do so. But the interests of the Nation must always come before any personal considerations.

From the discussions I have had with Congressional and other leaders, I have concluded that because of the Watergate matter, I might not have the support of the Congress that I would consider necessary to back the very difficult decisions and carry out the duties of this office in the way the interests of the Nation will require.

I have never been a quitter. To leave office before my term is completed is abhorrent[2] to every instinct in my body. But as President, I must put the interests of America first. America needs a full-time President and a full-time Congress, particularly at this time with problems we face at home and abroad.

To continue to fight through the months ahead for my personal vindication[3] would almost totally absorb the time and attention of both the President and the Congress in a period when our entire focus should be on the great issues of peace abroad and prosperity without inflation at home.

Therefore, I shall resign the Presidency effective at noon tomorrow. Vice President Ford will be sworn in as President at that hour in this office. . . .

---

1 **destabilizing:** making unstable

2 **abhorrent:** deeply contrary

3 **vindication:** clearance of blame; acquittal

By taking this action, I hope that I will have hastened the start of that process of healing which is so desperately needed in America.

I regret deeply any injuries that may have been done in the course of the events that led to this decision. I would say only that if some of my judgments were wrong—and some were wrong—they were made in what I believed at the time to be the best interest of the Nation.

To those who have stood with me during these past difficult months—to my family, my friends, to many others who joined in supporting my cause because they believed it was right—I will be eternally grateful for your support.

And to those who have not felt able to give me your support, let me say I leave with no bitterness toward those who have opposed me, because all of us, in the final analysis, have been concerned with the good of the country, however our judgments might differ.

So, let us all now join together in affirming that common commitment and in helping our new President succeed for the benefit of all Americans. . . . ❧

Nixon, daughter Tricia, and wife Pat after Nixon's resignation speech, 1974.

Waiting for the Barbarians

CONSTANTIN CAVAFY

THE OLD KING
1916–36
Georges Roualt

What are we waiting for, assembled in the forum?

    The barbarians[1] are due here today.

Why isn't anything happening in the senate?
Why do the senators sit there without legislating?

    Because the barbarians are coming today.
    What laws can the senators make now?
    Once the barbarians are here, they'll do the legislating.

1 **barbarians:** people who lack learning, culture, and refinement

Why did our emperor get up so early,
and why is he sitting at the city's main gate
on his throne, in state, wearing the crown?

> Because the barbarians are coming today
> and the emperor is waiting to receive their leader.
> He has even prepared a scroll to give him,
> replete with titles, with imposing names.

Why have our two consuls and praetors[2] come out today
wearing their embroidered, their scarlet togas?

Why have they put on bracelets with so many amethysts,
and rings sparkling with magnificent emeralds?
Why are they carrying elegant canes
beautifully worked in silver and gold?

> Because the barbarians are coming today
> and things like that dazzle the barbarians.

Why don't our distinguished orators come forward as usual
to make their speeches, say what they have to say?

> Because the barbarians are coming today
> and they're bored by rhetoric[3] and public speaking.

Why this sudden restlessness, this confusion?
(How serious people's faces have become.)
Why are the streets and squares emptying so rapidly,
everyone going home so lost in thought?

> Because night has fallen and the barbarians have not come.
> And some who have just returned from the border say
> there are no barbarians any longer.

And now, what's going to happen to us without barbarians?
They were, those people, a kind of solution.

---

2 **praetors:** government officials in Ancient Rome

3 **rhetoric:** formal speaking or writing

The One Who Watches

Judith Ortíz Cofer

"**M**ira! Mira!"[1] my friend Yolanda yells out. She's always telling me to look at something. And I always do. I look, she does. That's the way it's always been. Yolanda just turned sixteen, I'm six months younger. I was born to follow the leader, that's what my mother says when she sees us together, and it's true.

It's like the world is a deli full of pricey treats to Yolanda, and she wants the most expensive ones in fancy boxes, the ones she can't afford. We spend hours shopping downtown. Sometimes when Yolanda gets excited about an outfit, we go into the store and she tries it on. But the salespeople are getting to know us. They know we don't have any money. So we get chased out of places a lot. Yolanda always yells at the security man, "I've been thrown out of better places than this!" And we have.

One time Yolanda and I skipped school and took a bus into the city— just because Yolanda wanted to look around the big store on Thirty-fourth Street. They were having a teen fashion show that day, for all the rich girls in New York and their overdressed mothers. And guess what? Yolanda sneaked into one of the dressing rooms, with me following her, and she actually got in line for one of the dresses being handed out by all these busy-looking women with tape measures around their necks who called all the girls "honey" and measured their chest, waist, and hips in about thirty seconds flat. Then this guy in a purple skintight body suit screeches out, "Hey, you!" and I nearly pass out, thinking we had gotten caught.

---

1 **mira:** Spanish for "look"

"Those earrings are monstrous!" he screams at Yolanda, who's wearing pink rubber fish earrings to match her pink-and-black-striped minidress.

"Here, try these!" He hands her a set of gold hoops in a very fancy black velvet box; then he screams at another model. I go into a dressing stall to hide and Yolanda runs in and sits on my lap, laughing her head off.

"Mira, Doris, mira." She shows me the earrings, which look like real gold. I hug Yolanda—I just love this girl. She's crazy and will try anything for fun.

I help Yolanda put on the dress she says she's going to model. The price tag inside says $350.00. It's my turn to say "Mira" to Yolanda. She shrugs.

"I ain't gonna steal it, Doris," she says. "I'm just gonna walk down that runway, like this." She walks out of the dressing room with one hand on a hip, looking like a real model in a green velvet dress, gold earrings, and her white sneakers. The man in the body suit runs up to her, screaming, "No, no! What do you think you're doing? Those shoes are monstrous!" He waves over one of the women with measuring tapes around their necks and has her take down Yolanda's shoe size. Soon I'm helping her try on shoes from a stack as tall as I am. She decides on black patent leather pumps.[2]

There's such confusion back there that Yolanda doesn't get caught until the girls are lined up for the show to begin. Then nobody can find Yolanda on the list. She really does a good job of acting offended at all the trouble. I think it's her New Jersey Puerto Rican accent that gives her away. The others talk with their noses way up in the air, sounding like they have a little congestion.

"Whaddaya mean my name ain't there?" Yolanda demands, sticking her nose up there in orbit too.

I just stand to the side and watch everything, pretending that it's a play and Yolanda is the star. I promise myself that if it gets too dangerous, I'll just slip out. See, I'm not flashy like Yolanda. I'm practically invisible. My hair is kinky, so I keep it greased down, and I'm short and plain. Not ugly, not beautiful. Just a nothing. If it wasn't for Yolanda, nobody would know I'm around. She's great, but she scares me, like the modeling thing at the store. I have enough problems without getting arrested. So I tell myself

2 **patent leather pumps:** close-fitting woman's dress shoes with high to moderate heels, made out of leather with a glossy surface

that if the police come, I'll just make myself invisible and walk away. Then I'd be really alone. If Yolanda knew how scared I really am, she'd leave me anyway. Yolanda always says that nothing scares her except scared people. She says she hates a snitch worse than anything, and that's what scared people do, she tells me. They blame others for their troubles. That's why she dumped her last best friend, Connie Colón. Connie got scared when her mother found out she'd been skipping school with Yolanda, and told. Yolanda gets a cold look in her eyes when she talks about Connie, like she wants her dead. I don't want Yolanda to ever look at me that way.

Anyway, a big bossy woman came to lead us to her office on the top floor. It was bigger than my bedroom and her desk was at least the size of my bed. There was a rug under our feet that was as thick as a fur coat. From her window you could see most of New York. She looked at Yolanda with an expression on her face like I see on people walking by street people. It's like they want to ask them, "What are you doing on *my* sidewalk?" The lady didn't even look at me, so I glued myself to the gray wall.

"Young lady, do you realize that what you did today could be considered a crime?" She spoke very slowly, sounding out each word. I guess she knew by now that we were Puerto Rican and wanted to make sure we understood.

Yolanda didn't answer. They had made her take off the velvet dress, the shoes, and the earrings. The woman who carried them out with her fingertips put them in a plastic bag before handing them to this woman in front of us now.

Holding up the plastic bag in front of Yolanda, she asked another question: "Do you know how much money the things you took are worth?"

I watched Yolanda get up slowly from tying her shoestrings. She put on her pink fish earrings next without any hurry. Then she straightened out her tight skirt. She still looked offended. And maybe like she wanted a fight.

"I wasn't stealing your *theengs*," she said, imitating the woman's uptown accent.

"Then what were you doing in our dressing room, trying to disrupt the fashion show?"

"No. I was going to model the dress." Yolanda put her hands on her hips as if daring the woman to argue with her.

"Model? You wanted to model clothes *here?*" The woman laughed. "Young lady—"

"My name is Yolanda." Yolanda was getting angry, I could tell by the way she made her eyes flash at the woman, like a cat getting ready to pounce. It was strange to watch Yolanda, who is barely five feet tall, facing off with this big woman in a gray suit and high heels.

"All right, Yolanda. Let me tell you something. You can't just decide to be a model, sneak into a dressing room, and go on a runway. These girls have been to modeling school. They have been practicing for weeks. Did you really think you could get away with this?" She was sounding angry now. I edged toward the door. "I'll tell you what. I'm not going to turn you in. I'm going to have our security guard escort you outside. And I never want to see you in this store again. Look." She pointed to a camera practically invisible on the ceiling.

"We have pictures of you now, Yolanda." She finally looked over at me. "And of your partner there. If you come back, all I have to do is show them to the judge."

We were shown the way out to Thirty-fourth Street by the security guard, who looked just like any rich shopper in his wool sweater and expensive jeans. You never know who's watching you.

So Yolanda is telling the truth when she tells the store people that we've been thrown out of better places. She's always looking for a better place to get thrown out of. But the Thirty-fourth Street store may be hard to beat.

That same day we went up to the eighty-sixth floor of the Empire State Building—it's just down the street from the store. Yolanda went all around the viewing deck like a child, yelling out, "Mira! Mira!" from every corner. She was feeling good.

At home there is always salsa music[3] playing, but it's not because anyone is happy or feels like dancing. To my parents music is a job. They're both in a Latino music band called ¡Caliente![4] He plays the drums and she sings, so they're always listening to tapes. They play at the same barrio[5] club every night, the Caribbean Moon, and the regular customers want to hear new songs every week. So Mami sings along with the tapes, but she looks bored while she's doing it. Most of my life she stopped singing only to tell me to do something or to yell at me. My father doesn't say much. He's hardly ever around during the day; either he sleeps until the

---

3 **salsa music:** Latin American music that combines elements of rhythm and blues, jazz, and rock

4 **caliente:** Spanish for "hot"

5 **barrio:** Spanish for "neighborhood" or "slum"

afternoon, since they play sets until three in the morning, or he goes down to the basement to practice his drums. The super of our building, Tito, is his best friend and lets Papi keep his drums in a storage room near the washers and dryers. Our apartment has walls thin and crumbly as old cardboard, and if he tried to play drums in it they'd probably crash around our heads.

My mother is singing along with Celia Cruz, the old Cuban *salsera*,[6] when I come in. She's at the stove, sautéing some codfish. I can smell the olive oil simmering, but I'm not hungry. Yolanda and I ate a whole bagful of butterscotch candy. She wouldn't tell me where she got it and I never saw her buy it, although I spent the whole day with her.

"Hola,[7] Doris, how's school?" my mother asks. But she doesn't look at me and she doesn't wait for me to answer. She just keeps on singing something about leaving the cold American city and going home to a lover in the sun. I stand there watching her; I'm feeling invisible again. The tape ends and she asks me where I've been, since school let out hours ago.

"New York."

She finally looks at me and smiles as if she doesn't believe me. "I bet you've been following that Yolanda around again. Niña,[8] I'm telling you that señorita[9] is trouble. She's trying to grow up too fast, sabes?[10] Mira . . ." Mami takes my chin into her hand that smells like oregano and garlic and other Island spices. She looks really tired. She's short like me and we look a lot alike, but I don't think she's noticed. "Doris, tonight is not a school night, why don't you come to the club with us and listen to some music?" She's asked me to do that once a week for years, but I'm not interested in hanging out at a cheap nightclub with a bunch of drunks. Besides, I'd have to sit in the back the whole time because I'm a minor. In case the police do a check—I can slip out the kitchen door. When I was little, I had to go with them a lot, and it wasn't fun. I'd rather stay home by myself.

I shake my head and go into my room. I put a pillow over my face so I won't hear the music and my mother singing about people in love and islands with beaches and sun.

---

6 **salsera:** Spanish for "singer of salsa music"

7 **hola:** Spanish for "hello"

8 **niña:** Spanish for "girl"

9 **señorita:** Spanish for "young lady"

10 **sabes?:** Spanish for "do you know?"

I spend all day Saturday at Yolanda's. We have the place to ourselves because her mother works weekends. She believes in spiritism,[11] so there are candles everywhere with things written on the glass jars like "For money and luck," and "For protection against your enemies," and "To bring your loved one home." She's got a little table set up as an altar with statues of *santos*[12] and the Virgin Mary, and a picture of her dead husband, Yolanda's father, who was killed during a robbery. Yolanda says she doesn't remember him that well anymore, even though it's only a couple of years since he died.

The place is stuffy with incense smells, and Yolanda tells me we are going shopping today.

"You got money?" I notice that she's wearing a big raincoat of her mother's. It's made of shiny bright green plastic and it has huge pockets. I start feeling a little sick to my stomach and almost tell her I'm going home to bed.

"I got what it takes, honey." Yolanda models the ugly raincoat for me by turning around and around in the small room.

We have to pass my apartment on our way out, and I can hear my mother singing an old song without the usual music tape accompanying her in the background. I stop to listen. It's "Cielito Lindo"—a sort of lullaby that she used to sing to me when I was little. Her voice sounds sweet, like she is really into the song for once. Yolanda is standing in front of me with her hands on her hips, giving me a funny look like she thinks I'm a sentimental baby. Before she says something sarcastic, I run down the stairs.

Yolanda is not just window-shopping today. She tells me that she's seen something she really wants. When we get to the store—one of the most expensive ones downtown—she shows me. It's a black beaded evening bag with a long strap. She puts it on over her shoulder.

"It's cute," I tell her, feeling sicker by the minute. I want to get out of the store fast, but I'm too weak to move.

"You really like it, Doris?" Yolanda unlatches the flap on the purse and takes out the crumpled paper in it. She reaches into her pocket for a fistful of candy. "Want some?" In one motion she has stuffed the little bag into her coat pocket.

"Yolanda . . . " I finally begin to feel my legs under me. I am moving back, away from the scene that starts happening really fast in front of

11 **spiritism:** the view that spirits have the power to guide events in people's lives
12 **santos:** Spanish for "saints"

me, as if someone had yelled "Action!" on a movie set. Yolanda is standing there eating candy. I am moving backward even as she tries to hand me some. A man in a gray suit is moving toward her. I am now behind a rack of purses. I smell the leather. It reminds me of my father's drums that he used to let me play when I was little. Yolanda looks around, but she can't see me. I'm still moving back toward the light of the door. I know that I can't act scared, that I shouldn't run. People look at me. I know they can see me. I know where my arms are, where my legs are, where my head is. I am out on the street in the sun. A woman with a baby carriage bumps into me and says, "Excuse me!" She can see me! I hear a police car siren getting louder as I hurry across the street. I walk faster and faster until I am running and the world is going by so fast that I can't tell what anyone else is doing. I only hear my heart pounding in my chest.

When I crash through the door at home, Mami comes out of the bedroom looking like she just woke up from a deep sleep. I lie down on the sofa. I am sweating and shaking; a sick feeling in my stomach makes me want to curl up. Mami takes my head into her hands. Her fingers are warm and soft. "Are you sick, hija?"[13] I nod my head. Yes. I am sick. I am sick of following Yolanda into trouble. She has problems that make her act crazy. Maybe someday she'll work them out, but I have to start trying to figure out who I am and where I want to go before I can help anybody else. I don't tell my mother any of this. It's better if I just let her take care of me for a little while.

Even as she feels my forehead for fever, my mother can't help humming a tune. It's one I used to know. It's a song about being lonely, even in a crowd, and how that's the way life is for most people. But you have to keep watching out for love because it's out there waiting for you. That's the chorus, I mean. I keep my eyes closed until the words come back to me, until I know it by heart. And I know that I will keep watching but not just watching. Sometimes you have to run fast to catch love because it's hard to see, even when it's right in front of you. I say this to Mami, who laughs and starts really singing. She is really into it now, singing like she was standing in front of hundreds of people in Carnegie Hall,[14] even though I'm the only one here to hear her. The song is for me. ∾

---

13 **hija:** Spanish for "daughter"

14 **Carnegie Hall:** a famous recital hall in New York City

RESPONDING TO CLUSTER ONE

WHAT INFLUENCES A DECISION?

Thinking Skill ANALYZING

1. Use a chart to **analyze** a decision the main character makes in each selection. List the decisions; then look for influences. An example has been done for you.

Character	Decision	Influences
Josh in "Playing God"	leave home	Laurel's upcoming move; unhappy home situation
Speaker in "Dusting"		
Holly in "TLA"		
Richard Nixon in "I would have preferred to carry through"		
Doris in "The One Who Watches"		

2. In "I would have preferred to carry through," Richard Nixon makes a decision that goes against his personal wishes. Why do you think he makes this decision?

3. Choose one of the following subtitles for "Waiting for the Barbarians": *It's Easier to Let Someone Else Decide* or *So We Can Avoid Responsibility*. Explain your choice.

4. Most decisions involve both positive and negative consquences. In "The One Who Watches," for example, Doris makes a decision that will keep her out of trouble but will cost her a friendship. **Analyze** a decision from another selection and list both the positive and negative effects.

5. Of all the characters in this cluster, who makes the most difficult decision? Why?

Writing Activity: Analyzing the Decision-Making Process

Analyze the two quotations below. Then pick the one with which you agree, giving examples from either your own decisions or those of characters in this cluster.

"We can try to avoid making choices by doing nothing, but even that is a decision."
—Gary Collins

"One's mind has a way of making itself up in the background, and it suddenly becomes clear what one means to do."
—A. C. Benson

A Strong Analysis

- carefully examines the topic
- supports each point with evidence
- ends with a summary of ideas presented

CLUSTER TWO

Good Decision or Bad Decision?
Thinking Skill   EVALUATING

A Kind of Murder

HUGH PENTECOST

You might say this is the story of a murder—although nobody was killed. I don't know what has become of Mr. Silas Warren, but I have lived for many years with the burden on my conscience of having been responsible for the existence of a walking dead man.

I was fifteen years old during the brief span of days I knew Mr. Silas Warren. It was toward the end of the winter term at Morgan Military Academy. Mr. Etsweiler, the chemistry and physics teacher at Morgan, had died of a heart attack one afternoon while he was helping to coach the hockey team on the lake. Mr. Henry Huntingdon Hadley, the headmaster,[1] had gone to New York to find a replacement. That replacement was Mr. Silas Warren.

I may have been one of the first people to see Mr. Warren at the Academy. I had been excused from afternoon study period because of a heavy cold, and allowed to take my books to my room to work there. I saw Mr. Warren come walking across the quadrangle[2] toward Mr. Hadley's office, which was located on the ground floor under the hall where my room was.

Mr. Warren didn't look like a man who was coming to stay long. He carried one small, flimsy suitcase spattered with travel labels. Although it was a bitter March day he wore a thin, summer-weight topcoat. He stopped beside a kind of brown lump in the snow. That brown lump was Teddy, the school dog.

---

1 **headmaster:** director of a school
2 **quadrangle:** a four-sided area surrounded by buildings

Teddy was an ancient collie. They said that in the old days you could throw a stick for Teddy to retrieve until you, not he, dropped from exhaustion. Now the old, gray-muzzled dog was pretty much ignored by everyone except the chef, who fed him scraps from the dining room after the noon meal. Teddy would be at the kitchen door, promptly on time, and then find a comfortable spot to lie down. He'd stay there until someone forced him to move.

Mr. Warren stopped by Teddy, bent down, and scratched the dog's head. The old, burr-clotted tail thumped wearily in the snow. Mr. Warren straightened up and looked around. He had narrow, stooped shoulders. His eyes were pale blue, and they had a kind of frightened look in them. *He's scared,* I thought; *coming to a new place in the middle of a term, he's scared.*

I guess most of the other fellows didn't see Mr. Warren until he turned up at supper time at the head of one of the tables in the dining room. We marched into the dining room and stood behind our chairs waiting for the cadet major to give the order to be seated. The order was delayed. Mr. Henry Huntingdon Hadley, known as Old Beaver because of his snowy white beard, made an announcement.

"Mr. Warren has joined our teaching staff to fill the vacancy created by the unfortunate demise[3] of Mr. Etsweiler." Old Beaver had false teeth and his s's whistled musically. "I trust you will give him a cordial welcome."

"Be seated," the cadet major snapped.

We sat. Old Beaver said grace. Then we all began to talk. I was at Mr. Warren's right. He had a genial, want-to-be-liked smile.

"And your name is?" he asked me in a pleasant but flat voice.

"Pentecost, sir."

He leaned toward me. "How's that?" he asked.

"Pentecost, sir."

Sammy Callahan sat across from me on Mr. Warren's left. Sammy was a fine athlete and a terrible practical joker. I saw a gleam of interest in his eyes. As Mr. Warren turned toward him Sammy spoke in an ordinary conversational tone. "Why don't you go take a jump in the lake, sir?"

Mr. Warren smiled. "Yes, I guess you're right," he said.

Sammy grinned at me. There was no doubt about it—Mr. Warren was quite deaf!

---

3 **demise:** end; in this case, death

It was a strange kind of secret Sammy and I had. We didn't really know what to do with it, but we found out that night. Old Beaver was not a man to start anyone in gradually. It would have been Mr. Etsweiler's turn to take the night study hour, so that hour was passed on to Mr. Warren.

He sat on the little platform at the head of the study hall—smiling and smiling. I think there must have been terror in his heart then. I think he may even have been praying.

Everyone seemed unusually busy studying, but we were all waiting for the test. The test always came for a new master the first time he had night study hour. There would be a minor disturbance and we'd find out promptly whether this man could maintain discipline, or not. It came after about five minutes—a loud, artificial belch.

Mr. Warren smiled and smiled. He hadn't heard it.

Belches sprang up all over the room. Then somebody threw a handful of torn paper in the air. Mr. Warren's smile froze.

"Now, now boys," he said.

More belches. More torn paper.

"Boys!" Mr. Warren cried out, like someone in pain.

The Old Beaver appeared, his eyes glittering behind rimless spectacles. There was something I never understood about Old Beaver. Ordinarily his shoes squeaked. You could hear him coming from quite a distance away—squeak-squeak, squeak-squeak. But somehow, when he chose, he could approach as noiselessly as a cat, without any squeak at all. And there he was.

The study hall was quiet as a tomb. But the silence was frighteningly loud, and the place was littered with paper.

"There will be ten demerit marks[4] against every student in this room," Old Beaver said in his icy voice. "I want every scrap of paper picked up instantly."

Several of us scrambled down on our hands and knees. Mr. Warren smiled at the headmaster.

"Consider the lilies of the field," Mr. Warren said. "They toil not, neither do they spin. Yet I tell you that Solomon in all his glory—"

There was an uncontrollable outburst of laughter.

"Silence!" Old Beaver hissed, with all the menace of a poised cobra.

---

4 **demerit marks:** records of misbehavior, usually involving a loss of privilege

He turned to Mr. Warren. "I'll take the balance of this period, Mr. Warren. I suggest you go to your room and prepare yourself for tomorrow's curriculum."

▲　▲　▲

I didn't have any classes with Mr. Warren the next day, but all you heard as you passed in the corridors from one class period to the next were tales of the jokes and disorders in the physics and chemistry courses. Somehow nobody thought it was wrong to take advantage of Mr. Warren.

The climax came very quickly. In the winter, if you weren't out for the hockey or winter sports teams, you had to exercise in the gym. There were the parallel bars, and the rings, and the tumbling mats. And there was boxing.

The boxing teacher was Major Durand, the military commandant.[5] I know now that he was a sadist.[6] Major Durand was filled with contempt for everyone but Major Durand. I saw the look on his face when Mr. Warren appeared.

Mr. Warren had been assigned to help in the gym. He was something to see—just skin and bones. He had on a pair of ordinary black socks and, I suspect, the only pair of shoes he owned—black oxfords. He'd borrowed a pair of shorts that could have been wrapped twice around his skinny waist. Above that was a much mended short-sleeved undershirt. He looked around, hopeless, amiable.[7]

"Mr. Warren!" Major Durand said. "I'd like you to help me demonstrate. Put on these gloves if you will." He tossed a pair of boxing gloves at Mr. Warren, who stared at them stupidly. One of the boys helped him tie the laces.

"Now, Mr. Warren," Durand said. The Major danced and bobbed and weaved, and shot out his gloves in short vicious jabs at the air. "You will hold your gloves up to your face, sir. When you're ready you'll say 'Hit!'—and I shall hit you."

I'd seen Major Durand do this with a boy he didn't like. You held up the gloves and you covered your face and then, with your throat dry and aching, you said "Hit!"—and Major Durand's left or right would smash

---

5 **commandant:** commanding officer

6 **sadist:** someone who enjoys being cruel

7 **amiable:** friendly; good-natured

through your guard and pulverize[8] your nose or mouth. It was sheer strength I know now, not skill.

Mr. Warren held up his gloves, and he looked like an actor in an old Mack Sennett[9] comedy—the absurd clothes, the sickly smile.

Durand danced in front of him. "Whenever you say, Mr. Warren. Now watch this, boys. The feint[10]—and the jab."

"Hit!" said Mr. Warren, his voice suddenly falsetto.[11]

Pow! Major Durand's left jab smashed through the guard of Mr. Warren's nose. There was a sudden geyser of blood.

"Again, Mr. Warren!" the Major commanded, his eyes glittering.

"I think I'd better retire to repair the damage," Mr. Warren said. His undershirt was spattered with blood and he had produced a soiled handkerchief which he held to his nose. He hurried out of the gym at a sort of shambling gallop.

That night the payoff came in study hall. Mr. Warren was called on this time to substitute for Old Beaver, who had taken over for him the night before. Sammy Callahan staged it. Suddenly handkerchiefs were waved from all parts of the room—handkerchiefs stained red. Red ink, of course.

"Hit!" somebody shouted. "Hit, hit!" Nearly all the boys were bobbing, weaving, jabbing.

Mr. Warren, pale as a ghost, cotton visibly stuffed in one nostril, stared at us like a dead man.

Then there was Old Beaver again.

Somehow the word was out at breakfast the next morning. Mr. Warren was leaving. He didn't show at the breakfast table. I felt a little squeamish about it. He hadn't been given a chance. Maybe he wasn't such a bad guy.

It was during the morning classroom period that we heard it. It was a warm day for March and the ice was breaking up on the lake. The scream was piercing and terrified. Somebody went to the window. The scream came again.

"Somebody's fallen through the ice!"

---

8 **pulverize:** smash; demolish

9 **Mack Sennett:** director and performer in the Keystone Kops films—silent movies of the twenties

10 **feint:** move meant to mislead opponent; trick

11 **falsetto:** an artificially high voice

The whole school—a hundred and fifty boys and masters—hurried down to the shore of the lake. The sun was so bright that all we could see was a dark shape flopping out there, pulling itself up on the ice and then disappearing under water as the ice broke. Each time the figure rose there was a wailing scream.

Then the identification. "It's Teddy!" someone shouted.

The school dog. He'd walked out there and the ice had caved in on him. The screams were growing weaker. A couple of us made for the edge of the ice. Old Beaver and Major Durand confronted us.

"I'm sorry, boys," Old Beaver said. "It's a tragic thing to have to stand here and watch the old dog drown. But no one—no one connected with the school—is to try to get to him. I'm responsible for your safety. That's an order."

We stood there, sick with it. Old Teddy must have seen us because for a moment there seemed to be new hope in his strangled wailing.

Then I saw Mr. Warren. He was by the boathouse, his old suitcase in his hand. He looked out at the dog, and so help me there were tears in Mr. Warren's eyes. Then, very calmly, he put down his bag, took off his thin topcoat and suit jacket. He righted one of the overturned boats on the shore and pulled it to the edge of the lake.

"Mr. Warren! You heard my order!" Old Beaver shouted at him.

Mr. Warren turned to the headmaster, smiling. "You seem to forget, sir, I am no long connected with Morgan Military Academy, and therefore not subject to your orders."

"Stop him!" Major Durand ordered.

But before anyone could reach him, Mr. Warren had slid the flat-bottomed rowboat out onto the ice. He crept along on the ice himself, clinging to the boat, pushing it across the shiny surface toward Teddy. I heard Mr. Warren's thin, flat voice.

"Hold on, old man! I'm coming."

The ice gave way under him, but he clung to the boat and scrambled up—and on.

"Hold on, old man!"

It seemed to take forever. Just before what must have been the last, despairing shriek from the half-frozen dog, Mr. Warren reached him. How he found the strength to lift the watersoaked collie into the boat, I don't know; but he managed, and then he came back toward us, creeping along the cracking ice, pushing the boat to shore.

The chef wrapped Teddy in blankets, put him behind the stove in the kitchen, and gave him a dose of warm milk and cooking brandy. Mr. Warren was hustled to the infirmary.[12] Did I say that when he reached the shore with Teddy the whole school cheered him?

Old Beaver, for all his tyranny,[13] must have been a pretty decent guy. He announced that night that Mr. Warren was not leaving after all. He trusted that, after Mr. Warren's display of valor, the boys would show him the respect he deserved.

I went to see Mr. Warren in the infirmary that first evening. He looked pretty done in, but he also looked happier than I'd ever seen him.

"What you did took an awful lot of courage," I told him. "Everybody thinks it was really a swell thing to do."

Mr. Warren smiled at me—a thoughtful kind of smile. "Courage is a matter of definition," he said. "It doesn't take courage to stand up and let yourself get punched in the nose, boy. It takes courage to walk away. As for Teddy—somebody had to go after him. There wasn't anyone who could but me, so courage or not, I went. You'd have gone if Mr. Hadley hadn't issued orders." He sighed. "I'm glad to get a second chance here. Very glad."

Somehow I got the notion it was a last chance—the very last chance he'd ever have.

▲ ▲ ▲

It was a week before Mr. Warren had the night study hall again. It was a kind of test. For perhaps fifteen minutes nothing happened and then I heard Sammy give his fine, artificial belch. I looked up at Mr. Warren. He was smiling happily. He hadn't heard. A delighted giggle ran around the room.

I was on my feet. "If there's one more sound in this room I'm going after Old Beaver," I said. "And after that I'll personally take on every guy in this school if necessary, to knock sense into him!"

The room quieted. I was on the student council and I was also captain of the boxing team. The rest of the study period was continued in an orderly fashion. When it was over and we were headed for our rooms, Mr. Warren flagged me down.

"I don't know quite what was going on, Pentecost," he said, "but I gather you saved the day for me. Thank you. Thank you very much.

12 **infirmary:** medical clinic
13 **tyranny:** oppressive power

Perhaps when the boys get to know me a little better they'll come to realize—" He made a helpless little gesture with his bony hands.

"I'm sure they will, sir," I said. "I'm sure of it."

"They're not cruel," Mr. Warren said. "It's just high spirits, I know."

Sammy Callahan was waiting for me in my room. "What are you, some kind of a do-gooder?" he said.

"Give the guy a chance," I said. "He proved he has guts when it's needed. But he's helpless there in the study hall."

Sammy gave me a sour grin. "You and he should get along fine." he said. "And you'll need to. The guys aren't going to be chummy with a do-gooder like you."

It was a week before Mr. Warren's turn to run the study hour came around again. In that time I'd found that Sammy was right. I was being given the cold shoulder. Major Durand, who must have hated Mr. Warren for stealing the heroic spotlight from him, was giving me a hard time. One of the guys I knew well came to me.

"You're making a mistake," he told me. "He's a grown man and you're just a kid. If he can't take care of himself it's not your headache."

I don't like telling the next part of it, but it happened. When Mr. Warren's night came again, the study hall was quiet enough for a while. Then came a belch. I looked up at Mr. Warren. He was smiling. Then someone waved one of those fake bloody handkerchiefs. Then, so help me, somebody let out a baying howl—like Teddy in the lake.

Mr. Warren knew what was happening now. He looked down at me, and there was an agonizing, wordless plea for help in his eyes. I—well, I looked away. I was fifteen. I didn't want to be called a do-gooder. I didn't want to be snubbed. Mr. Warren *was* a grown man and he should have been able to take care of himself. The boys weren't cruel: they were just high spirited—hadn't Mr. Warren himself said so?

I looked up from behind a book. Mr. Warren was standing, looking out over the room. His stooped, skinny shoulders were squared away. Two great tears ran down his pale cheeks. His last chance was played out.

Then he turned and walked out of the study hall.

No one ever saw him again. He must have gone straight to his room, thrown his meager belongings into the battered old suitcase, and taken off on foot into the night.

You see what I mean when I say it was a kind of murder?

And I was the murderer. ❧

DAVID GRAVES PEMBROKE STUDIOS LONDON TUESDAY, 27TH APRIL 1982
1982
David Hockney

Trapped in the Desert

GARY BEEMAN

It began innocently enough, that hot June night, when I turned off U.S. 91 in the middle of the Mojave Desert[1] and headed the old black coupe[2] down a gravel road. I was only 18, and I didn't understand how a moment of thoughtlessness in the midsummer desert can lead you, step by irrevocable step, to disaster.

An aged prospector had told us—my 16-year-old school friend Jim Tworney and me—that the road led to derelict Rasor Ranch, on the edge of an area called the Devil's Playground. Desert "ghost settlements" fascinated me, and so did the prospector's report of rattlesnakes there. As a budding zoology major, I collected animal specimens to help pay for such wandering vacations as this.

We had a couple of days' food in the car, and there was supposed to be a good well at Rasor. Still, I'd never have turned off the highway with only two pints of water in our canteens if I hadn't been so tired. It was almost midnight. We'd driven more than 400 miles from San Francisco; then we'd bird-watched most of the sun-scorched afternoon.

Turning off the highway at a half-buried tire the prospector had told us about, I drove down the moonlit gravel road. After a long way—I didn't notice just *how* long—we hit a little finger of sand that had drifted across the road. I gunned the car, and we plowed over it, then over three more drifts.

---

1 **Mojave Desert:** a desert in Southern California
2 **coupe:** a small, two-door car, often with seating for only two

After the fourth, our headlights showed no firm gravel road, only pale, undulating[3] sand. For a few feet the car gained momentum. Then its spinning wheels began to dig down. We shuddered to a halt.

Obviously, I'd taken a wrong turn. We got out and paced the distance back to the road: 200 feet. Jim wanted to sleep and dig out next morning. "No," I said. "Let's get out now. It'll take only a few minutes."

An hour later, we hadn't moved an inch. The rear wheels had dug deeper, that was all. Then, searching for rocks in the moonlight, we stumbled onto the remains of an old railroad track. The steel had been salvaged,[4] but a few ties remained. We found nine in various degrees of preservation.

Using one as a firm base, we jacked up the car and laid a double strip of ties, starting at the front wheels and extending out behind. Then I eased the car backward. It moved slowly but steadily: two feet—six feet—ten feet. Then one wheel slipped off a tie and the car stopped.

All through that long, frustrating night we jacked up the car, rearranged the ties, reversed a few feet until the inevitable slip. I figured we'd come at least 12 miles from the highway, perhaps 20. But what really mattered was that 200 feet of sand between the car and the gravel road. By five o'clock in the morning we'd covered perhaps 50 feet—still 150 to go. Exhausted, we drank all but two cupfuls of our water, then slept on the bare sand.

Almost at once, it seemed, the sun was beating fiercely down. Now, in stark daylight, things looked more serious. We could see why this sand-bowl was called the Devil's Playground. Only scraggly bushes broke the barren, stony slopes. Ahead, a dry soda lake glared blindingly white.

Stripped to the waist, we went to work on the car. Within half an hour the sun was burning our skin. The sand soon grew too hot to touch. "Let's rest till evening," I suggested. "We'll get her out once it cools down." Jim didn't need much persuading. We decided we'd shelter in one of the rock faces of a hill that thrust up a quarter mile across the sand. I still wasn't really worried. In fact, before we left the car I shot a few feet of movie film.

We found two shady hideaways, 30 feet apart. Sprawled under a shallow overhang, I dozed fitfully. The sunlight moved steadily closer, beating savagely up from the pale sand. Soon a bare foot of shade remained. My lips began to crack.

---

3 **undulating:** rising up and down
4 **salvaged:** reclaimed; saved

About noon we shared the last two cupfuls of water. Afterward, I lay and watched the line of sunlight, waiting for it to retreat. I kept wondering how hot it really was.

At last, a wedge of shade moved up unexpectedly from one side. The sun set; a wonderful coolness fell. Somewhere out in the desert, a whippoorwill began its plaintive song. Jim and I went down to the car and ate our first food in 24 hours—the first we'd wanted. We each finished a can of chicken noodle soup—preheated by the inferno inside the black coupe—then shared the juice from a small can of pineapple.

The food revived us, and we discussed whether to try walking out. Jim felt too weak for such a long trek, and I rated my own chances at a bare 50-50. We decided to keep working on the car. I didn't really grasp, even then, that we were in desperate danger. I knew that unwary motorists had died of thirst in the desert; not long before, in Death Valley just 30 miles to the north, the dried-out corpses of two young men had been found close beside their stalled car. But somehow I felt it couldn't happen to us.

My memories of that second night are blurred. It was all we could do to jack up the car and run it back a few feet until it slipped off the disintegrating ties. We kept resting, I remember, and half-dozing. About four o'clock we fell asleep.

When I awoke, the half-risen sun was already burning my skin like an infrared lamp. Every movement demanded effort. And now for the first time I understood our peril: During the night we had moved the car barely 15 feet; more than 130 feet remained! Jim, weak and listless, seemed to have lost hope. With rocks and twigs I laid out a four-foot S.O.S.;[5] then we started toward our rock shelters.

Right from the start, that second day was terrible. Even in my shady overhang, I could feel the heat sucking moisture out of my body. And it wasn't only the heat. The silence was almost as bad. I found myself straining for sounds, but all I could hear was my heartbeat. The drumbeat inside me swamped everything.

Occasionally I'd hear Jim's heavy breathing. Then he began to babble, in dream or delirium.[6] "What about my grape drink?" he kept saying. "I've paid for it, and I want my grape drink." At last he fell silent.

Soon, the noonday sun was pressing my strip of shade tight against

---

5 **S.O.S.:** international signal for help

6 **delirium:** temporary confusion due to illness or a high fever

the overhang. Once, I heard the lisp of sifting sand. Four feet away a rattlesnake was moving past, from shade to shade.

I lay in a daze now, never quite dozing, never fully awake. I had given up hope that the day would ever pass its peak. Once, when I squinted out at the car, shimmering in the heat haze a quarter mile away, there was another car parked beside our coupe—and a stream of vehicles rushing up and down the black highway on which they stood. Had I, after all, walked out to the highway? I twisted my head; then squinted out again; the old black coupe stood on pale sand, alone.

Panic swept me. I knew dehydration eventually unbalances your mind. If I could already see a nonexistent highway, had I been *acting* irrationally?

At last, in midafternoon, I could stand the terrible dryness no longer. Struggling to my feet, I went out into the sun. When I looked down toward the car, I saw for the first time that the flat sand near it had once been a lake. "If I dig," I thought, "perhaps I'll find water." I staggered down the hill.

There were green-leaved creosote bushes growing on a small sand dune, and I remembered that when digging for lizards in such places I had found moisture. I began digging into the side of the dune, in among the bushes' roots. There was no water; but suddenly I realized that my hands felt almost cool. Perhaps I could dig a cave and crawl into that wonderful coolness!

I don't know how long it took me to scoop out a hole. But at last it was big enough. I stripped off all my sweat-grimed clothes and crawled in. The cool sand soothed me like a balm. I fell asleep.

I woke to see the sun sinking below a line of hills. The plaintive whistle of my whippoorwill came at last. I felt cool and rested. Then, without warning, Jim staggered past. His head lolled;[7] his arms hung loose at his sides. Suddenly he sank to one knee, then pitched forward and lay still. I shook him. He moaned faintly.

Alarmed, I hurried to the car and searched feverishly through the inferno inside it. Under the seat I found bottle of aftershave lotion. I wrenched off the top and put it to my lips. The shock of what tasted like hot rubbing alcohol brought me up short. Again I had that horrible, fleeting comprehension of my unhinged state of mind.

I began rubbing lotion on my face and neck. It felt good. So I went

---

7 **lolled:** hung loosely; drooped

back to Jim, rubbed lotion on his face and poured it over his T-shirt. He was deathly pale, his mouth hung open, and dried mucus flecked his scaly white lips. "We need a drink," I kept thinking. "We both need a drink."

Desperately, I ran my eyes over the car. And suddenly I was thinking, *"The radiator!"* I'd always known that in the desert your radiator water could save you; yet for two days I'd ignored it! I grabbed a saucepan, squirmed under the front bumper and unscrewed the radiator drainage tap. A stream of rust-brown water poured down over the greasy sway bar and splashed into my saucepan. It was the most wonderful sight I had ever seen.

Still lying under the car, I took several huge gulps. The water was thick with oil and rust. Almost at once, though, I began to feel better. When I had drained the radiator and filled a canteen, I went back to Jim and poured water into his open mouth. He stirred.

Then I returned to the car, got a can of chow mein and ate half of it. Soon Jim was sitting up and eating his half of the chow mein.

My mind felt clearer, and I realized that if we were to get out I'd have to try something new. After a while I saw what would have been obvious if I had been thinking clearly: That I would have to run the car back off the ties at high speed and just hope I could keep it going.

We were still pitifully weak. When Jim tried to help he collapsed over the jack, and the rest of that third night he lay prostrate.[8] I must have spent five or six hours over a job that would normally take 20 minutes: aligning the car perfectly on the ties for our final attempt. I knew that if we failed the first time I wouldn't have the strength to try again. At last, utterly exhausted, I fell asleep.

I awoke in hot sunlight. Hurriedly, we drank the last of the water. I helped Jim into the car, started the motor, and let it idle for a few moments. Then I looked at Jim, sprawled across the seat. "This is it," I said. He didn't seem to hear.

I revved the motor, slammed the automatic transmission into reverse and stamped on the accelerator. The car leaped backward. It gained speed, slipped off the ties . . . kept going. All at once, a tie banged hard, somewhere up front. The car faltered, almost stopped. Then the tie snapped, and we were moving again.

But soon we were slowing down. The rear wheels started to dig in with

---

| 8 **prostrate:** flat; overcome

a horribly familiar sinking motion. They would spin, grip for a moment, then spin again. And, all the time, the motor was slowing down, the car sinking into the sand. We'd almost stopped when I felt the tires grab something solid. They spun again . . . grabbed and spun . . . grabbed. For interminable[9] moments we hung poised between life and death. Then the tires took firm grip and we were moving smoothly. At last we were out on the gravel road, and I was whooping like an idiot. Beside me, Jim was smiling weakly.

Four hours later, after many sweltering halts for the now-dry motor to cool, we turned onto the highway; we'd been stuck only six miles off U.S. 91. And within another mile—less than seven from the desolate sand-bowl where we'd faced a terrible death—we came to a modern roadside cafe.

"Kinda warm today, boys," the man behind the counter said. Then he took another look at us and saw that we were drained dry, caked with grime and dead tired.

He put two glasses of water on the counter. "Just sip it a little, boys," he said, "until you get used to it." ∾

---

9 **interminable:** endless; eternal

Traveling Through the Dark

WILLIAM STAFFORD

Traveling through the dark I found a deer
dead on the edge of the Wilson River road.
It is usually best to roll them into the canyon:
that road is narrow; to swerve might make more dead.

By glow of the tail-light I stumbled back of the car
and stood by the heap, a doe, a recent killing;
she had stiffened already, almost cold.
I dragged her off; she was large in the belly.

My fingers touching her side brought me the reason—
her side was warm; her fawn lay there waiting,
alive, still, never to be born.
Beside that mountain road I hesitated.

The car aimed ahead its lowered parking lights;
under the hood purred the steady engine.
I stood in the glare of the warm exhaust turning red;
around our group I could hear the wilderness listen.

I thought hard for us all—my only swerving—;
then pushed her over the edge into the river.

SPRING
1947
Ben Shahn
© Estate of Ben Shahn/Licensed by VAGA, New York, NY

Long Walk to Forever

BY KURT VONNEGUT, JR.

They had grown up next door to each other, on the fringe of a city, near fields and woods and orchards, within sight of a lovely bell tower that belonged to a school for the blind.

Now they were twenty, had not seen each other for nearly a year. There had always been playful, comfortable warmth between them, but never any talk of love.

His name was Newt. Her name was Catharine. In the early afternoon, Newt knocked on Catharine's front door.

Catharine came to the door. She was carrying a fat, glossy magazine she had been reading. The magazine was devoted entirely to brides. "Newt!" she said. She was surprised to see him.

"Could you come for a walk?" he said. He was a shy person, even with Catharine. He covered his shyness by speaking absently, as though what really concerned him were far away—as though he were a secret agent pausing briefly on a mission between beautiful, distant, and sinister points. This manner of speaking had always been Newt's style, even in matters that concerned him desperately.

"A walk?" said Catharine.

"One foot in front of the other," said Newt, "through leaves, over bridges—"

"I had no idea you were in town," she said.

"Just this minute got in," he said.

"Still in the Army, I see," she said.

"Seven more months to go," he said. He was a private first class in the Artillery. His uniform was rumpled. His shoes were dusty. He needed a shave. He held out his hand for the magazine. "Let's see the pretty book," he said.

She gave it to him. "I'm getting married, Newt," she said.

"I know," he said. "Let's go for a walk."

"I'm awfully busy, Newt," she said. "The wedding is only a week away."

"If we go for a walk," he said, "it will make you rosy. It will make you a rosy bride." He turned the pages of the magazine. "A rosy bride like her—like her—like her," he said, showing her rosy brides.

Catharine turned rosy, thinking about rosy brides.

"That will be my present to Henry Stewart Chasens," said Newt. "By taking you for a walk, I'll be giving him a rosy bride."

"You know his name?" said Catharine.

"Mother wrote," he said. "From Pittsburgh?"

"Yes," she said. "You'd like him."

"Maybe," he said.

"Can—can you come to the wedding, Newt?" she said.

"That I doubt," he said.

"Your furlough[1] isn't for long enough?" she said.

"Furlough?" said Newt. He was studying a two-page ad for flat silver. "I'm not on furlough," he said.

"Oh?" she said.

"I'm what they call A.W.O.L.,"[2] said Newt.

"Oh, Newt! You're not!" she said.

"Sure I am," he said, still looking at the magazine.

"Why, Newt?" she said.

"I had to find out what your silver pattern is," he said. He read names of silver patterns from the magazine. "Albemarle? Heather?" he said. "Legend? Rambler Rose?" He looked up, smiled. "I plan to give you and your husband a spoon," he said.

"Newt, Newt—tell me really," she said.

"I want to go for a walk," he said.

She wrung her hands in sisterly anguish. "Oh Newt—you're fooling me about being A.W.O.L.," she said.

---

1 **furlough:** a leave of absence from duty

2 **A.W.O.L.:** an abbreviation for "absent without leave"

Newt imitated a police siren softly, raised his eyebrows.

"Where—where from?" she said.

"Fort Bragg," he said.

"North Carolina?" she said.

"That's right," he said. "Near Fayetteville—where Scarlett O'Hara went to school."

"How did you get here, Newt?" she said.

He raised his thumb, jerked it in a hitchhike gesture. "Two days," he said.

"Does your mother know?" she said.

"I didn't come to see my mother," he told her.

"Who did you come to see?" she said.

"You," he said.

"Why me?" she said.

"Because I love you," he said. "Now can we take a walk?" he said. "One foot in front of the other—through leaves, over bridges—"

▲   ▲   ▲

They were taking the walk now, were in a woods with a brown-leaf floor.

Catharine was angry and rattled, close to tears. "Newt," she said, "this is absolutely crazy."

"How so?" said Newt.

"What a crazy time to tell me you love me," she said. "You never talked that way before." She stopped walking.

"Let's keep walking," he said.

"No," she said. "So far, no farther. I shouldn't have come out with you at all," she said.

"You did," he said.

"To get you out of the house," she said. "If somebody walked in and heard you talking to me that way, a week before the wedding—"

"What would they think?" he said.

"They'd think you were crazy," she said.

"Why?" he said.

Catharine took a deep breath, made a speech. "Let me say that I'm deeply honored by this crazy thing you've done," she said. "I can't believe you're really A.W.O.L., but maybe you are. I can't believe you really love me, but maybe you do. But—"

"I do," said Newt.

"Well, I'm deeply honored," said Catharine, "and I'm very fond of you as a friend, Newt, extremely fond—but it's just too late." She took a step away from him. "You've never even kissed me," she said, and she protected herself with her hands. "I don't mean you should do it now. I just mean this is all so unexpected. I haven't got the remotest idea of how to respond."

"Just walk some more," he said. "Have a nice time."

They started walking again.

"How did you expect me to react?" she said.

"How would I know what to expect?" he said. "I've never done anything like this before."

"Did you think I would throw myself into your arms?" she said.

"Maybe," he said.

"I'm sorry to disappoint you," she said.

"I'm not disappointed," he said. "I wasn't counting on it. This is very nice, just walking."

Catharine stopped again. "You know what happens next?" she said.

"Nope," he said.

"We shake hands," she said. "We shake hands and part friends," she said. "That's what happens next."

Newt nodded. "All right," he said. "Remember me from time to time. Remember how much I loved you."

Involuntarily, Catharine burst into tears. She turned her back to Newt, looked into the infinite colonnade[3] of the woods.

"What does that mean?" said Newt.

"Rage!" said Catharine. She clenched her hands. "You have no right—"

"I had to find out," he said.

"If I'd loved you," she said, "I would have let you know before now."

"You would?" he said.

"Yes," she said. She faced him, looked up at him, her face quite red. "You would have known," she said.

"How?" he said.

"You would have seen it," she said. "Women aren't very clever at hiding it."

Newt looked closely at Catharine's face now. To her consternation, she realized that what she had said was true, that a woman couldn't hide love.

<hr />

3 **colonnade:** a series of columns set at regular intervals

Newt was seeing love now.

And he did what he had to do. He kissed her.

▲ ▲ ▲

"You're hell to get along with!" she said when Newt let her go.

"I am?" said Newt.

"You shouldn't have done that," she said.

"You didn't like it?" he said.

"What did you expect," she said—"wild, abandoned passion?"

"I keep telling you," he said, "I never know what's going to happen next."

"We say good-by," she said.

He frowned slightly. "All right," he said.

She made another speech. "I'm not sorry we kissed," she said. "That was sweet. We should have kissed, we've been so close. I'll always remember you, Newt, and good luck."

"You too," he said.

"Thank you, Newt," she said.

"Thirty days," he said.

"What?" she said.

"Thirty days in the stockade," he said—"that's what one kiss will cost me."

"I—I'm sorry," she said, "but I didn't ask you to go A.W.O.L."

"I know," he said.

"You certainly don't deserve any hero's reward for doing something as foolish as that," she said.

"Must be nice to be a hero," said Newt. "Is Henry Stewart Chasens a hero?"

"He might be, if he got the chance," said Catharine. She noted uneasily that they had begun to walk again. The farewell had been forgotten.

"You really love him?" he said.

"Certainly I love him!" she said hotly. "I wouldn't marry him if I didn't love him!"

"What's good about him?" said Newt.

"Honestly!" she cried, stopping again. "Do you have any idea how offensive you're being? Many, many, many things are good about Henry! Yes," she said, "and many, many, many things are probably bad too. But that isn't any of your business. I love Henry, and I don't have to argue his merits with you!"

"Sorry," said Newt.

"Honestly!" said Catharine.

Newt kissed her again. He kissed her again because she wanted him to.

▲　▲　▲

They were now in a large orchard.

"How did we get so far from home, Newt?" said Catharine.

"One foot in front of the other—through leaves, over bridges," said Newt.

"They add up—the steps," she said.

Bells rang in the tower of the school for the blind nearby.

"School for the blind," said Newt.

"School for the blind," said Catharine. She shook her head in drowsy wonder. "I've got to go back now," she said.

"Say good-by," said Newt.

"Every time I do," said Catharine, "I seem to get kissed."

Newt sat down on the close-cropped grass under an apple tree. "Sit down," he said.

"No," she said.

"I won't touch you," he said.

"I don't believe you," she said.

She sat down under another tree, twenty feet away from him. She closed her eyes.

"Dream of Henry Stewart Chasens," he said.

"What?" she said.

"Dream of your wonderful husband-to-be," he said.

"All right, I will," she said. She closed her eyes tighter, caught glimpses of her husband-to-be.

Newt yawned.

The bees were humming in the trees, and Catharine almost fell asleep. When she opened her eyes she saw that Newt really was asleep.

He began to snore softly.

Catharine let Newt sleep for an hour, and while he slept she adored him with all her heart.

The shadows of the apple trees grew to the east. The bells in the tower of the school for the blind rang again.

"*Chick-a-dee-dee-dee,*" went a chickadee.

Somewhere far away an automobile starter nagged and failed, nagged and failed, fell still.

Catharine came out from under her tree, knelt by Newt.

"Newt?" she said.

"H'm?" he said. He opened his eyes.

"Late," she said.

"Hello, Catharine," he said.

"Hello, Newt," she said.

"I love you," he said.

"I know," she said.

"Too late," he said.

"Too late," she said.

He stood, stretched groaningly. "A very nice walk," he said.

"I thought so," she said.

"Part company here?" he said.

"Where will you go?" she said.

"Hitch into town, turn myself in," he said.

"Good luck," she said.

"You, too," he said. "Marry me, Catharine?"

"No," she said.

He smiled, stared at her hard for a moment, then walked away quickly.

Catharine watched him grow smaller in the long perspective of shadows and trees, knew that if he stopped and turned now, if he called to her, she would run to him. She would have no choice.

Newt did stop. He did turn. He did call. "Catharine," he called.

She ran to him, put her arms around him, could not speak. ❧

Facing Donegall Square

MARIA TESTA

A bomb went off in Belfast[1] yesterday. The sirens began howling only minutes before the blast, while I stood in the middle of the Gap, of all places, with a pair of jeans draped over my arm, thanking God that I had just got out of the dressing room in time. The sirens I could handle, but being caught with my pants down during a moment of civil crisis might have finished me off.

The sales people sprang into action, and a woman with a quivering smile snatched the jeans from my hands, promising me that I could pick them up later, whatever that meant. I really liked the way those jeans fit, too. People were trying not to panic, running toward the very same doors that the army, or the police, or whoever the guys with the automatic weapons might be, were charging through.

"Get out! Get out!" the army guys shouted, but I just stood there, somehow convinced that my American citizenship granted me some kind of immunity.[2]

A security guard grabbed me by the shoulders and shoved me toward the door.

"Come on, love, move!" he roared as I turned my face away from him, not wanting him to read in my eyes, in my expression, what I had suddenly realized.

---

1 **Belfast:** the capital of the troubled country of Northern Ireland (Ireland and Northern Ireland occupy the same island, but are separate countries.) Problems in Northern Ireland include conflicts between Protestants and Catholics, as well as violent protests against British rule.

2 **immunity:** protection from danger

I knew who planted the bomb.

▲   ▲   ▲

It wasn't my idea to go to Belfast in the first place. I was perfectly content to stay in Dublin[3] with my sister, Allie, who was studying at Trinity College. Allie was the first person in our family to go to college at all, and she wanted to make the most of it by spending her junior year in Ireland. I was supposed to be the second college-bound family member, which was the only reason Mom let me spend spring break with my "positive-influence-on-you" big sister.

I had looked forward to a fun and wild Irish vacation, during which Allie and I would roam the streets of Dublin, on the lookout for poets and musicians. Especially musicians. But Allie had a thesis[4] due that term on some eighteenth-century Irish guy, and, of course, she would settle for nothing less than an honors grade. And the only possible way to earn an honors grade, she said, was to spend a day combing through historical documents at the Public Records Office of Northern Ireland. She actually seemed excited about it.

In any event, three days before I was supposed to return to the States, we caught the 8:00 A.M. train out of Dublin and arrived in Belfast two hours later.

"I'm going to get lost," I said for the seventeenth time, as our black cab stopped in the middle of beautiful, barbed-wired Belfast. The driver laughed. Allie smiled, but I could tell her patience was wearing thin. Allie had presented me with an unusually creative idea moments before our train had pulled into the station. She would do her research alone while I explored the city—also alone. In other words, my sister was ditching me. I was not impressed.

"Look, Julie," Allie said as she rolled down the cab window. "This is City Hall." She pointed to a huge, official-looking building. "This whole block is called Donegall Square. The shopping district is across the street. There are all kinds of restaurants and shops there. Whenever you get confused, just face Donegall Square. I'll meet you there at four. You can't possibly get lost." She sounded totally convinced.

I looked at my sister, with her thick auburn hair and dark eyes. How could two people who look so much alike be so unbelievably different?

---

3 **Dublin:** the capital of Ireland, 150 miles south of Belfast
4 **thesis:** a scholarly paper

Allie was the studious type, craving solitude, while I was a true social animal with, by my own admission, something of a tendency to run off at the mouth. I knew Allie was smart to get rid of me if she wanted to get anything done. But no way was I going to let her get away guilt-free.

"Mom's going to kill you when she finds out you took me here," I said. "You know she's got this thing about war-torn cities."

"Come on, Julie, get out," Allie said. "This place is safer than any American city. You'll be fine." I stared at her, convinced that my only sister in the world lacked a soul.

I climbed out of the cab and faced Donegall Square. The driver pulled off, and Allie held up four fingers through the open window. Four o'clock. Just six hours to go. I was overcome with joy.

▲   ▲   ▲

I shouldn't have been nervous. I mean, I wasn't exactly an experienced world traveler, but I'd been around the proverbial[5] block more than a couple of times. Like most kids from my neighborhood back home, I had seen my share of drugs and guns. I should have been prepared for anything. But my American street bravado disappeared along with my sister. I did not want to be alone.

Any way you look at it, I didn't exactly start out on the right foot. Actually, I did start out on my right foot, glancing quickly to the left as I stepped off the curb. Of course, since I was in Belfast, the traffic was barreling toward me from the right. I froze.

"Watch it, Miss!" a voice called out from behind me. Someone grabbed my arm, yanking me back on the sidewalk.

I liked him immediately. I imagined that I would probably feel a certain degree of affection for just about anyone who saved my life, but I really liked the way this particular hero looked. He was probably a year or two older than I was, maybe even eighteen, but he was wearing one of those school uniforms every high school kid in all of Ireland is required to wear. It made him look younger, and I liked his shaggy hair and easy smile. He shifted his backpack.

"I'd say you're an American," he said. There wasn't a trace of doubt in his voice.

"My stupidity gave me away?"

---

5 **proverbial:** familiar because it comes from a frequently used proverb, or saying

"No, no! That's not what I meant," he said with a quick laugh. A very nice hand landed on my shoulder. He seemed to appreciate my sense of humor. Definitely a plus.

"On your way to school?" I asked, glancing at his backpack. It looked heavy. "Looks like you had a lot of homework."

"Ah, we always do," he said. "But I don't have a class for another hour or so."

"And I don't have a life for the next six hours. My sister's left me stranded until four."

He picked up the hint. "May I escort you across the street then, Miss?" He offered his arm, gentleman-style. Why be shy? I wrapped my arm around his.

"My name's Julie," I said.

"Mine's Seamus."

It crossed my mind that I just might be in love.

▲ ▲ ▲

Seamus and I had a fun, if unproductive, time together. I mentioned that I could use a new pair of jeans, so off we went, in search of jeans that would satisfy my cultivated American tastes. We darted in and out of a lot of interesting, offbeat little shops, but all I really wanted was another pair of faded Levi's. Finally, Seamus suggested we take a break and stop for tea.

"Sorry I couldn't help you find what you're looking for," he said. He set down our tray on a table near the cafe window.

"And I'm sorry I kept you for so long," I said. "I think you missed your next class."

"Don't worry about it." Seamus waved his hand. "I can afford to miss a class or two. Especially when the options are so appealing." His eyes actually twinkled. I felt privileged to be there, as a witness.

"Seamus," I said, after a moment. "Do you mind if I ask you a question?" He didn't respond immediately. He poured the tea slowly, then carefully folded his hands in front of him.

"Okay."

I took a deep breath. "Why is there a security guard in the doorway of every shop, and why did they all make a point of watching every move you made?" I spoke quickly. I knew enough about the situation in Belfast to know that I was not asking easy questions.

"Julie, what religion are you?" Seamus asked. His voice was quiet, but clear.

"Catholic," I practically whispered. I felt like I was telling a secret.

"You see this emblem?" Seamus pointed to the chest pocket of his uniform jacket. I nodded. It was pretty hard to miss the purple and gold cross and staff. "That means I'm Catholic, too. And that means that I'm automatically a threat to the national security—or something momentous like that."

I detected at least a trace of bitterness in his voice, but I was struck more by the calmness, the evenness of his tone.

"I'm sorry," I said.

Seamus shrugged. "It's life." He leaned over and kissed me on the cheek. "But I do have to go to my next class," he said. "Physics, you know." He stood up and hoisted his backpack onto his shoulders. I imagined it filled with heavy physics books. He must be brilliant, I thought. I just had to try to see him again.

"I have an idea," I said. "I'm supposed to meet my sister at four in front of City Hall. Do you think you could meet us there and maybe have dinner or something before we have to go back to Dublin?"

Seamus smiled. I really wanted him to say yes.

"I'd love to. I would," he said. "But let me see how the rest of the day goes. If everything goes smoothly, I'll be there. But if something comes up—you know, at school or whatever—I won't be able to make it. You know how it is."

"Believe me, I do," I said. "You can't even imagine how many times I've had to stay after school."

Seamus laughed. "Actually," he said, "I think I probably can." He leaned over again, kissed me on the other cheek, and then, quickly, he was out the door.

I sighed. I glanced at my watch. Four more hours to kill. I decided to hang out in the cafe for a while and relive the last two hours, before heading out to continue my search for a new pair of jeans.

▲ ▲ ▲

I was surprised when I found the Gap. It was a large, modern building, part of a whole arcade of new stores. It would have been the obvious place to shop for American jeans. I wondered why Seamus hadn't taken me there.

Fifteen minutes later, when I was in the middle of a crowd sprinting up the street away from the sound of a bomb exploding, I didn't wonder anymore.

Idiot! I screamed at myself silently. No high school kid just shows up at school in the middle of the day. No one carries around a backpack that heavy. Everyone knows you can buy American jeans at the Gap. Idiot.

But I knew I was being too tough on myself. Seamus was good, very good. He didn't give me any real clues. We just spent a nice morning together, that's all. Still, call it intuition, I knew Seamus had planted that bomb.

I was the first of the crowd to stop running. Somehow, being able to put a face behind the bomb made me less afraid. And then, suddenly, I was angry. My mind clicked in, sharp, clear, focused. I felt like I was back home, ready to think on my feet. Okay, I thought, he can't be far away. The army had occupied the whole block almost immediately. Seamus had to be hiding somewhere.

I walked up another block before crossing over to backtrack. If I wandered back behind the bombing scene, I might be relatively inconspicuous. And if someone did approach me, I knew I could pull off a little lost American girl routine. I was well aware, however, that if I suspected Seamus was still in the area, the police would, too. I wasn't sure if I cared who found him first.

▲　▲　▲

I almost didn't recognize him when I saw him. I was cutting across a junkyard of sorts, outside the police barriers, and there he was, about twenty yards away, crouched between an abandoned refrigerator and a heap of scrap metal. The backpack was gone, and he was wearing different clothes—jeans and a black sweater—but that wasn't why he looked so different.

His whole being had changed. He seemed shriveled, tiny, his eyes darting left and right, and when those eyes found mine, the nervousness turned to horror. He held up his hands and shook his head. I took a step backward, somehow aware of the danger of my presence.

"Miss! Miss!" a voice called from the distance, and a soldier was running toward me, an automatic weapon slung across his chest, black boots pounding on the pavement. Seamus dove inside the refrigerator, leaving the door open just a crack. I imagined him inside, afraid to breathe deeply, gasping for air.

Now is the time, I commanded myself, and I felt my hand rise to point to the refrigerator. I waved at the soldier instead.

"Hel-lo!" I called in my most innocent American accent.

The soldier stood in front of me, both hands on his gun. I decided not to see it.

"Can you help me?" I continued. "I'm lost. I'm supposed to meet my sister at City Hall." He studied me carefully, his suspicion turning to disgust.

"What are you doing here, love?" he asked. "This place is dangerous. City Hall is that way." He gestured behind him.

'I'm sorry," I said.

"Move along," he ordered. "Quickly."

I obeyed. I resisted the urge to glance back toward the refrigerator. I smiled at the soldier and turned to face Donegall Square. ✑

Responding to Cluster Two

Good Decision or Bad?
Thinking Skill EVALUATING

1. Authors usually choose titles carefully to convey meaning. What do you think the title "A Kind of Murder"means? Explain your reasons.

2. In each story listed below, the main character must make at least one decision. Using a chart such as the one below, describe a decision each character makes and **evaluate** it, telling why you think it was good or bad.

Character	Decision	Why It Was Good or Bad
Narrator in "A Kind of Murder"		
Gary in "Trapped in the Desert"		
Speaker in "Traveling Through the Dark"		
Catharine in "Long Walk to Forever"		
Julie in "Facing Donegall Square"		

3. Decisions are seldom all good or all bad. Select one of the decisions you **evaluated** in question two, and identify what changes might have occurred to turn this from a good to a bad decision or vice versa.

4. The **mood** of a piece of writing is its primary feeling or atmosphere. For example, a thriller is usually suspenseful and a comedy is often lighthearted. How would you describe the mood of the poem "Traveling Through the Dark"?

5. In "Facing Donegall Square," the narrator tells *what* she does but not *why* she does it. Why do you think she lets Seamus go free instead of pointing him out to the police?

Writing Activity: How to Make a Decision

Based on what you have learned so far about decision-making, write a how-to article for teenagers on making good decisions. (Hint: You will first want to review the decisions characters make in the stories. The chart in question 2 may help.)

A How-to Article

• takes the intended audience into account

• describes the task to be done

• tells how to do it in clear and easy steps

• concludes by encouraging the reader's attempt to do the task described

CLUSTER THREE

What Are The Possible Consequences of Our Decisions?

Thinking Skill PREDICTING

Ashes

SUSAN BETH PFEFFER

That winter, it felt like every time I saw my father, the sun cast off just a little more warmth than it had the day before. I don't remember a gray day when I saw him. Once it had snowed the night before, and getting to his apartment took longer than normal, as the buses inched their ways past snowbanks and awkwardly parked cars. But the sun made everything glisten, and the snow still had a pure look to it, which I knew would be gone by the following morning.

I saw him Tuesdays. I'd been seeing him Tuesdays for almost two years at that point. Before then, it had been Tuesdays and alternate weekends, but as my life got busier, weekends got harder, and Dad didn't complain when we fell instead into a Tuesday-evening ritual. Mom, who was still working on completing her degree, took Tuesday and Thursday evening classes, so I'd go straight to Dad's from school, wait for him to show, and then we'd have supper together and talk. It helped that he didn't live a hundred miles away. Just the other end of town, a two-bus-trip ride.

Dad drove me home Tuesday nights, and the moon always shone as brightly as the sun had and the winter stars looked joyful and beckoning. When I was little, Dad used to promise me the stars for a necklace, but like most of his promises, that one never quite happened.

"I'm a dreamer," he said to me more than once, which really wasn't all that different from what Mom said. "He's an irresponsible bum" was her way of wording it. I knew he was both, but I also knew that winter that the sun and the moon dreamed with him.

Sometimes when I haven't seen Dad for a few days, on a Saturday or a Sunday, I'll try figure out why Mom ever married him. She's the most practical person I know, always putting aside for a rainy day. With Mom, there are a lot of rainy days and she takes a grim sort of pleasure in being ready for them. The flashlight with working batteries for a blackout. The extra quarters when the laundry isn't quite dry. The gift-wrapped bottle of wine for the unexpected and undesired Christmas guest. Her pocketbook overflows with tissues for anyone who might need them.

Dad gets by on a grin and a willingness to help. He's always there if you need him. Well, not always. He's unexpectedly there, like a warm day in January. He's a rescuer. "I saw a woman stranded on the road," he'd say. "So I changed her tire for her." Or he took the box of kittens to the Humane Society, or he found the wallet with the ID intact, and returned it in person to its owner (and, of course, turned down a reward). He helps blind people cross the street and lost people find their way.

"I go to bed at night, and ask myself, 'Is the world a better place because I exist?'" he told me once. "If I've done one thing, no matter how small, that made the world a better place, I'm satisfied."

Of course no one ever got rich helping blind people cross the street. The world might be a better place, but child support checks don't always show up on time, and I never did get that necklace made of stars. Both Mom and Dad see to it I know his limitations.

"All I can give you is dreams, Ashes," he said to me once. "But one good dream is worth a thousand flashlight batteries."

Ashes. I can still hear the fight. It was just a couple of months before the final breakup. I was in bed, allegedly asleep, when they went at it.

"Her name is Ashleigh!" Mom shouted. "A name you insisted on. So why do you call her 'Ashes'?"

"That's just my nickname for her," Dad replied. He was always harder to hear when they fought. The angrier Mom got, the lower his voice dropped. For some reason, that made her shout even louder.

"But ashes are cold, gray, dead things," Mom yelled. "You're calling your daughter something dead!"

"It's just a nickname," Dad repeated, a little quieter.

"You call her that just to annoy me!" Mom yelled, but Dad's reply was so soft, I could no longer hear him.

A couple of days later, when Dad forgot to pick me up at school, or didn't have the money for the class trip, or got all his favorite kinds of Chinese and none of Mom's and mine, I thought maybe Mom was right, and Dad did call me Ashes just to annoy her. I made a list that evening of all the words that rhymed with ashes—smashes and crashes, trashes and bashes, clashes and mashes—and it didn't seem quite so nice anymore, having a special nickname. But then Dad gave me roses or sang a song he'd written for me. Or maybe he moved two buses away. And I realized he still called me Ashes, where Mom couldn't hear him to be annoyed. And that made me feel special all over again. Mom might never be caught without batteries or tissues, but she just called me Ashleigh—a name she didn't even like—and never promised me anything.

"Mom, can I have an extra five dollars to go to the movies this weekend?"

"I can't promise you that."

What could Dad have promised her to get her to love him? And what could Mom have offered to make Dad love her back? Whatever it was, it was dying by the time I was born, and dead before I turned six. Dad could make everyone in the world smile, except Mom. And Mom was always prepared, except for what Dad did to her.

It was toward the end of February that winter, and the sun was shining and the air was crisp and clean. I sat waiting for Dad, who I knew would show up eventually. I probably did my homework, or maybe I looked out the window for his car to show. The room he was renting didn't have a TV. Maybe there was a library book to read. Maybe I folded his laundry.

When he got in, he was full of smiles and kisses and I no longer resented the waiting, if I had resented it at all. "Ashes!" he cried, as though it had been years since we'd last seen each other, and not a simple week of overcast skies and bone-chilling weather. "Have you ever seen such a day!"

I had, seven days before. But I smiled at Dad, who always seemed to discover the weather each time we visited.

"You look radiant," he said. "You get more and more beautiful. Turn around. Let me admire every single inch."

So I turned around. I was wearing jeans and a bulky brown sweater Mom had given me for Christmas.

"You could be a model," Dad said. "Have you thought about that, Ashes. Modeling? Some of those supermodels make a fortune."

"Dad," I said. "I could never be a supermodel."

"Don't sell yourself short," he replied. "I've read interviews where they say they never thought they were pretty. Not in high school. Just tall and skinny. And you don't have to worry about being tall or skinny."

"I know, Dad," I said. "Which is why I'll never be a supermodel."

He looked at me and then he grinned. "All right," he said. "You're too smart for that kind of work anyway. Be a photographer instead, or a dress designer. You have flair, Ashes. Style. You do something like that, you're sure to make your mark."

Last week he'd told me to be an astronaut. The week before that, the CEO[1] of a Fortune 500 corporation. And the week before that, he'd been stunned by my spirituality.

"Oh, Ashes," he said, taking off his winter coat and dropping it on the sofa bed. "I wish I deserved you."

"I wouldn't have any other dad," I told him. "My friends' fathers, they just tell my friends to study more. They never tell them they have flair or style."

"Maybe they don't," Dad said. "You're the special one, Ashes. You're the one-in-a-million girl."

"Am I really?" I asked, not needing the reassurance. I knew I wasn't a one-in-a-million girl, no matter how often Dad told me I was. But no matter how often he told me, I still loved hearing him say it.

"One in a million," he said. "And don't let anyone ever tell you otherwise, Ashes. They will, you know. They'll try to tear you down. They'll laugh at your dreams. Even your mother—and she's a saint to have put up with me all those years—even she will discourage you from being all you can be. I hate to speak against her, but she's not a dreamer, Ashes. She's the most levelheaded woman I know. As straight as a yardstick. But I was the only dream she ever believed in and once I failed her, she never let herself dream again."

"Mom's all right," I said.

"She certainly is," Dad said. "She's a fine woman."

We were both silent as we pondered Mom. Then Dad laughed. "She'd never let you go hungry," he said. "What do you want for supper, Ashes? I can offer you pizza, Chinese, or fast."

"Anything," I said.

"No, no," he said, and he clapped his hands. "I remember. There's a new diner, opened right around the block. Let's treat ourselves, Ashes, and go out on the town."

"Can you afford it?" I asked, after doing the mental arithmetic of diner versus pizza.

---

1 **CEO:** chief executive officer, or top boss

"For a special date with my daughter?" he replied. "Of course I can afford it. Besides, I have something to celebrate."

"What?" I asked.

"I have a chance at something really big," he said. "All I need to do is put together a little financing, and I'll be set for life."

"For life?" I said, and I must have sounded like Mom because he stopped smiling.

"All right, not for life," he said. "But it'll be the start of something really big, Ashes. I can feel it. Just a couple hundred bucks, and then all the pieces will fall into place."

I had no idea where Dad thought he could get two hundred dollars. But he looked so happy I had to smile, too.

"Then diner it is," I said, and I got my coat. Dad picked his up from the sofa and put it back on. "Rice pudding for dessert," he said as we walked out the door. "You can always tell the quality of a diner by its rice pudding."

The diner might have been brand new, but already it had a shabby run-down quality that made it fit right in with the neighborhood. It was two-thirds empty when we got there, and we had our choice of booths. Dad took one that faced the door, and sat in the seat where he could check who was coming in. He hadn't done that with me in a long time, and my stomach hurt in an old familiar way.

"Waiting for someone?" I asked him. I stared at the menu, so I wouldn't have to look at him not looking at me.

"Of course not," he said. "Not when I'm with you. Take your pick, Ashes. Hamburger, triple-decker, chicken salad platter. Whatever you want."

I ordered the burger and fries, hoping that by the time it came I'd feel like eating. Dad took a quick look at the menu, closed it, and ordered coffee.

"You'll share my fries," I said to him.

He nodded as though we'd just completed a difficult negotiation. "I'll even eat your pickle," he said. But then he looked back at the door.

"What is it?" I asked him.

"It's nothing," he said. "Oh hell, Ashes, you can always see right through me."

He was the one who'd been looking right through me toward the door, but I didn't say anything.

"That money," he said. "The two hundred dollars?"

I nodded.

"Well it isn't so much for a deal as to help pay off one I already made," Dad said. "But I've got to tell you, honey, once that money is paid, I'm on my way to easy street. Just a little setback. But you know how those guys are. They get itchy when you owe them money. And it's not always comfortable to be where they can scratch you."

"You owe them two hundred dollars?" I asked, trying to keep the panic out of my voice.

"Give or take," Dad said. "But don't worry about it, honey. I'll work it out. I always do."

My burger and fries came then. Dad took a long sip of his coffee, while I poured ketchup on my plate and twirled a fry in it. "Can I help?" I asked.

Dad smiled like I'd offered him the key to the mint.[2] "I love you so much," he said. "You're ten thousand times better than I deserve, Ashes."

"Have a fry," I said, pushing my plate toward him. Dad took one. He seemed to have more of an appetite than I did.

"I had a thought," he said as he reached for my pickle. "Your mother keeps a couple hundred in cash at her place."

I didn't think either of us was supposed to know that.

"In that pretty teapot her mother gave her," Dad said. "Unless she's changed her hiding place. I know she changed the locks when I moved out, so maybe she changed her hiding place as well."

Sometimes, when Mom wasn't home, I'd take the lid off the teapot and stare into it, imagining what I could do with two hundred dollars. I looked at Dad and realized he'd had those same fantasies. Well, why not. I was his daughter, after all.

"The money's still in the teapot," I said.

Dad grinned. "She's a wonderful woman," he said. "But she gets one idea and she never wants to change it."

"What do you want to do, Dad?" I asked. "Come into the apartment with me and take the money?"

"Oh no," he said, and he looked really shocked. "That would be robbery, Ashes. I would never steal from your mother. I've caused her pain enough."

I took a bite of burger. Dad ate some more fries.

---

2 **key to the mint:** expression meaning access to unlimited money

"No, I just thought maybe you could borrow the money," he said. "Just for a day or two, until I straighten out all my finances. Your mother would never know the difference. Unless there's an earthquake or the Martians invade. I think we can gamble neither of those things will happen before Friday."

"You'll be able to pay her back by Friday?" I asked.

"You," Dad said. "I'd be borrowing the money from you. And I swear to you, Ashes, I'd have the money in your hands by Friday at the latest." He wiped his hand on his napkin and offered it to me as though to shake on the deal.

"Dad, I don't know," I said. "That's a lot of money. What if Mom finds out?"

"It's me she'd be angry at," Dad said. "Which is why she'll never find out. I wouldn't jeopardize our time together, honey. You let me have the money tonight, I'll straighten out my little difficulty, and Thursday night, when your mom is out, I'll give you back what I owe you. No earthquakes, no Martians, no problem."

I looked at the clock on the wall behind Dad. "Mom'll be home soon," I said.

"You all through?" he asked.

I nodded.

"Let's go, then," he said, the rice-pudding test long forgotten.

We went back to his place so I could pick up my books. Then we walked down to his car. "Why don't you sell your car?" I asked him. If he did that, I'd keep my hands clean, and Mom would never know. "You could get the money you need that way."

"You're your mother's daughter," he said. "Good head on your shoulders. Problem is, I'd never be able to find another car this cheap to replace it. No, Ashes, the teapot's the way to go."

We drove back to Mom's in silence. Usually we talked. Sometimes Dad sang one of his songs to me. For a moment, a cloud drifted past the moon and the sky turned greenish gray.

"Snow tomorrow," Dad said. "Maybe you'll get a snow day."

"Maybe," I said.

Dad parked the car a block away from Mom's. "Just in case she gets home early," he said. "I don't want her to see me waiting."

"Okay," I said.

"You go up to the apartment," he said. "Take the money, and come right down. Then I'll drop you off in front of her place, like always, and she'll never know the difference."

"What do I do if Mom's already there?" I asked.

"Just stay where you are," he said. "If you're not back here in ten minutes, I'll go home."

"All right," I said, and reached to unlock the door.

Dad touched me on my shoulder, gloved hand on winter coat. "You're one in a million," he said to me. "The best daughter a man could dream of."

I got out of the car and ran over to the apartment. I took the elevator to the tenth floor and unlocked the door. The apartment was quiet. It always felt a little colder when Mom wasn't there. Even with the lights turned on, it seemed a little darker.

I walked into the kitchen and turned on the light. The teapot was right where it belonged. I lifted its lid and stared at her emergency money. It was shaped like a little house, with a curtained window and a flowerpot on the windowsill. It was the sort of house I'd never lived in, probably never would with the amount of time it was taking Mom to finish her degree.

I stood over the teapot and stared at the money. Mom's emergency money. Her earthquake money. Her Martian money. Ten Andrew Jacksons[3] stared right back at me. They offered me no advice on what I should do.

I looked out the window and saw only ash gray sky. In the cold stillness of the night, I could hear my father's car keening[4] in the distance. "You're one in a million," it cried. ∾

---

3 **Andrew Jacksons:** slang for twenty-dollar bills, which have Andrew Jackson's picture on them

4 **keening:** making a loud, wailing sound

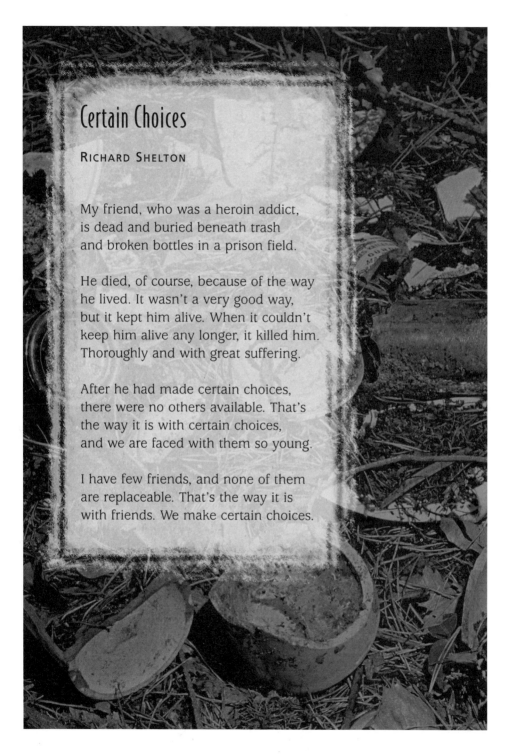

Certain Choices

RICHARD SHELTON

My friend, who was a heroin addict,
is dead and buried beneath trash
and broken bottles in a prison field.

He died, of course, because of the way
he lived. It wasn't a very good way,
but it kept him alive. When it couldn't
keep him alive any longer, it killed him.
Thoroughly and with great suffering.

After he had made certain choices,
there were no others available. That's
the way it is with certain choices,
and we are faced with them so young.

I have few friends, and none of them
are replaceable. That's the way it is
with friends. We make certain choices.

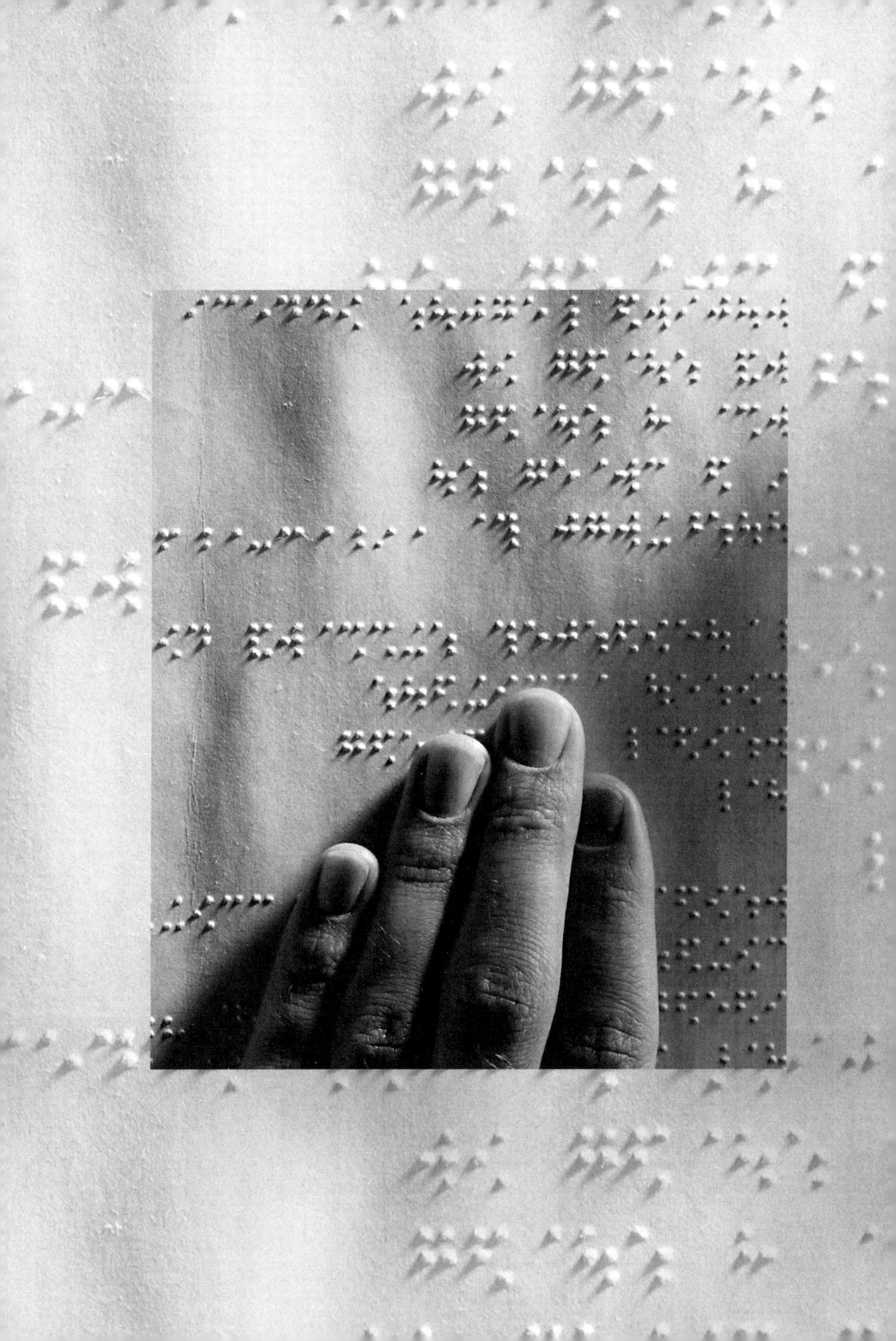

Moving into the Mainstream

SLADE ANDERSON, AGE 18

During junior high school I went to the New York Institute for Special Education, a school for the blind and visually impaired in the Bronx. It wasn't quite like a regular school. As a blind person I had practically everything I needed: Braille writers, talking computers, Braille books . . . I was able to run errands for teachers and help other kids get around school and understand their work.

But there were many things about the Institute that I didn't like. A lot of the students had other problems besides being visually impaired or totally blind. Some of them were off in their own worlds and used to talk to themselves, laugh out loud, mimic other people, or jump up and down and rock back and forth. (These weird habits are sometimes referred to as blindisms.)

And that wasn't all. Teachers and staff had to follow you around or know exactly where you were at all times. I hated that. I also hated having to get picked up by a school bus at 6:40 every morning. It was an hour and a half each way between my house in Brooklyn and the Institute, so there was no way I could hang out after school. And if I wanted to go around my own neighborhood, I had to go with my father, mother, or sister.

"What kind of teenage life is this?" I thought. I felt like only half a person.

I felt cut off from my friends from elementary school. I'd see some of them at the Lighthouse for the Blind on Saturdays. These were kids with little or no vision who were going to public school and taking mainstream classes.

My friend Billy was going to Edward R. Murrow, a public high school in Brooklyn. "You should come to Murrow, man. It's cool," he said. He talked about the girls there and the resource room where visually limited kids could go to have their work enlarged, put in Braille, or read out loud to them. Billy was making it in the real world and I wanted that for myself.

Another friend of mine, Mike, told me about the Christmas parties they had. It sounded like if I went to that school, I'd have everything I ever wanted: girls, friends, parties, popularity, and people to help me with my print work.

One day after going to the Lighthouse, I approached my mother about it. I told her I wanted to go to Murrow. I told her Billy went there along with other kids who were totally blind. "I want to broaden my social life," I said. "And my grades are good so I know I can do well in a mainstream class." The next day we took a bus ride just to see how far Murrow was from my house.

After that, I made an appointment to visit the school. When I got there, there were a million kids in the hallway. I went upstairs and met Mrs. Simon, the resource room teacher, and saw some of my old friends. Mrs. Simon asked my friend Chris to show me around. I'd never seen such a big school all in one building or met so many nice people. "You get around this big school without getting lost?" I asked Chris.

He just laughed and said, "You'll get it down in no time."

In one of the hallways I met a kid named Ricky who was totally blind. He had a guide dog and a lot of girls around him. "Just imagine that being me," I thought.

For the first week or so, my mother brought me to school. Then I started taking a school bus. Because I already knew so many people, had a resource room where I could get extra help, and was taking special ed. classes at first, the change from the Institute to Murrow wasn't too drastic.

In the resource room I had people dictate class notes, math problems, or whatever else I couldn't read on my own. The teachers assigned kids to take me from class to class, and if a kid couldn't take me, a teacher or a paraprofessional[1] would do it.

My friend Chris helped me get acclimated to the school. My first year we were in the school production of *The King and I* together. Chris (who

---

1 **paraprofessional:** a trained aide who assists a professional

has a little vision) helped me get around the stage and interact with the rest of the cast. Chris was very sociable, and knowing there was another person with limited vision getting along with the rest of the kids helped bring me out of my shell. It turned out to be a great experience.

As time progressed I started to take mainstream classes. The first one I remember setting foot into was Spanish. I had taken a little Spanish at the Institute and wanted to see how I'd do, so Mrs. Simon asked the teacher to let me sit in on the class. It moved at a much faster pace than the special ed. classes I was taking. The kids didn't stop the teacher quite as often either. They also behaved a little better.

The teacher gave us a list of new words. She'd say the word and then the whole class would repeat it. I could pretty much follow that. But when she started to give out handouts I really felt isolated. I took the handouts anyway and went over them later with someone in my resource room. A lot of the low vision kids had to do that or ask one of the kids next to them for help.

While I was working toward becoming mainstreamed, I also took mobility training. We made a tactual map (a raised map you can feel with your fingertips) of the school and I learned how the hallways and class-rooms were set up numerically. I also found my way around using landmarks like cracks on the floor, pillars, and garbage cans.

I worked on the bus trip to and from the school with Cindy, my mobil-ity teacher. We practiced getting to the bus stop, then taking the bus home, and finally making the trip to school. It took a lot of work but on the morning that she told me I was finally "cleared" to travel by myself, it was almost like getting a license to drive. That's how free I felt. It was a big accomplishment.

But mainstreaming isn't something that happens overnight and then you're done. You have to work at it. The bus I had to take didn't run very often and sometimes it would rush right past me without stopping. After a while I made friends with some of the drivers, though, and they would know to stop for me. One driver knew me so well that when I wasn't on his bus in the morning the next day he'd ask me, "Playing hooky again, huh?"

Even after I worked my way out of special ed. and was taking regular classes with sighted kids, I still had obstacles to overcome. During one cycle I had gym class on the fourth floor. To get there you had to go through two different gyms and up a flight of stairs. After I changed out of my gym clothes I never had enough time to get to math class. The teacher told me he didn't mind my being late, but I felt uncomfortable about it. It made me appear disabled.

Without consulting my resource room teacher I went straight to my guidance counselor and requested a schedule change. When Mrs. Simon heard about it she was upset. She felt I was going over her head—and getting in over mine. She said the class I had requested had a teacher who once had a bad experience with a blind student and she was concerned about that. I took the class anyway and got an "excellent."

With every success story there is a little hardship, however. People still shy away from me because I'm visually impaired. Sometimes instead of saying "Hi, Slade" they say, "Watch that stick." Others feel embarrassed if I ask them to read something to me softly.

Going into a mainstream program was a big and scary decision, but I'm still glad I made it. Life at the Institute was too sheltered. At Murrow I learned that I can't always have a Braille book handed to me at the same time the print users get theirs. I learned that there is life outside the blind world and if I want to be a part of it, I have to go out and take some risks. ◈

Button, Button

RICHARD MATHESON

The package was lying by the front door—a cube-shaped carton sealed with tape, their name and address printed by hand: "Mr. and Mrs. Aurthur Lewis, 217 E. Thirty-seventh Street, New York, New York 10016." Norma picked it up, unlocked the door, and went into the apartment. It was just getting dark.

After she put the lamb chops in the broiler, she sat down to open the package.

Inside the carton was a push-button unit fastened to a small wooden box. A glass dome covered the button. Norma tried to lift it off, but it was locked in place. She turned the unit over and saw a folded piece of paper Scotch-taped to the bottom of the box. She pulled it off: "Mr. Steward will call on you at 8:00 P.M."

Norma put the button unit beside her on the couch. She reread the typed note, smiling.

A few moments later, she went back into the kitchen to make the salad.

The doorbell rang at eight o'clock. "I'll get it," Norma called from the kitchen. Arthur was in the living room, reading.

There was a small man in the hallway. He removed his hat as Norma opened the door.

"Mrs. Lewis?" he inquired politely.

"Yes?"

"I'm Mr. Steward."

"Oh, yes." Norma repressed a smile. She was sure now it was a sales pitch.

"May I come in?" asked Mr. Steward.

"I'm rather busy," Norma said, "I'll get you your whatchamacallit, though." She started to turn.

"Don't you want to know what it is?"

Norma turned back. Mr. Steward's tone had been offensive. "No, I don't think so," she replied.

"It could prove very valuable," he told her.

"Monetarily?" she challenged.

Mr. Steward nodded. "Monetarily," he said.

Norma frowned. She didn't like his attitude. "What are you trying to sell?" she asked.

"I'm not selling anything," he answered.

Arthur came out of the living room. "Something wrong?"

Mr. Steward introduced himself.

"Oh, the—" Arthur pointed toward the living room and smiled. "What is that gadget, anyway?"

"It won't take long to explain," replied Mr. Steward. "May I come in?"

"If you're selling something—," Arthur said.

Mr. Steward shook his head. "I'm not."

Arthur looked at Norma. "Up to you," she said.

He hesitated. "Well, why not?" he said.

▲　▲　▲

They went into the living room and Mr. Steward sat in Norma's chair. He reached into an inside coat pocket and withdrew a small sealed envelope. "Inside here is a key to the bell-unit dome," he said. He set the envelope on the chair-side table. "The bell is connected to our office."

"What's it for?" asked Arthur.

"If you push the button," Mr. Steward told him, "somewhere in the world someone you don't know will die. In return for which you will receive a payment of $50,000."

Norma stared at the small man. He was smiling.

"What are you talking about?" Arthur asked him.

Mr. Steward looked surprised. "But I've just explained," he said.

"Is this a practical joke?" asked Arthur.

"Not at all. The offer is completely genuine."

"You aren't making sense," Arthur said. "You expect us to believe—"

"Whom do you represent?" demanded Norma.

Mr. Steward looked embarrassed. "I'm afraid I'm not at liberty to tell

you that," he said. "However, I assure you, the organization is of international scope."

"I think you'd better leave," Arthur said, standing.

Mr. Steward rose. "Of course."

"And take your button unit with you."

"Are you sure you wouldn't care to think about it for a day or so?"

Arthur picked up the button unit and the envelope and thrust them into Mr. Steward's hands. He walked into the hall and pulled open the door.

"I'll leave my card," said Mr. Steward. He placed it on the table by the door.

When he was gone, Arthur tore it in half and tossed the pieces onto the table.

Norma was still sitting on the sofa. "What do you think it was?" she asked.

"I don't care to know," he answered.

She tried to smile but couldn't. "Aren't you curious at all?"

"No." He shook his head.

After Arthur returned to his book, Norma went back to the kitchen and finished washing the dishes.

"Why won't you talk about it?" Norma asked.

Arthur's eyes shifted as he brushed his teeth. He looked at his reflection in the bathroom mirror.

"Doesn't it intrigue you?"[1]

"It offends me," Arthur said.

"I know, but"—Norma rolled another curler in her hair—"doesn't it intrigue you, too?"

"You think it's a practical joke?" she asked as they went into the bedroom.

"If it is, it's a sick one."

Norma sat on her bed and took off her slippers. "Maybe it's some kind of psychological research."

Arthur shrugged. "Could be."

"Maybe some eccentric millionaire is doing it."

"Maybe."

"Wouldn't you like to know?"

Arthur shook his head.

"Why?"

"Because it's immoral," he told her.

Norma slid beneath the covers. "Well, I think it's intriguing," she said.

Arthur turned off the lamp and leaned over to kiss her. "Good night," he said.

"Good night." She patted his back.

Norma closed her eyes. Fifty thousand dollars, she thought.

▲   ▲   ▲

In the morning, as she left the apartment, Norma saw the card halves on the table. Impulsively, she dropped them into her purse. She locked the front door and joined Arthur in the elevator.

While she was on her coffee break, she took the card halves from her

---

1 **intrigue you:** spark curiosity in you

purse and held the torn edges together. Only Mr. Steward's name and telephone number were printed on the card.

After lunch, she took the card halves from her purse again and Scotch-taped the edges together. "Why am I doing this?" she thought.

Just before five, she dialed the number.

"Good afternoon," said Mr. Steward's voice.

Norma almost hung up but restrained herself. She cleared her throat. "This is Mrs. Lewis," she said.

"*Yes,* Mrs. Lewis," Mr. Steward sounded pleased.

"I'm curious."

"That's natural," Mr. Steward said.

"Not that I believe a word of what you told us."

"Oh, it's quite authentic," Mr. Steward answered.

"Well, whatever—" Norma swallowed. "When you said someone in the world would die, what did you mean?"

"Exactly that," he answered. "It could be anyone. All we guarantee is that you don't know them. And, of course, that you wouldn't have to watch them die."

"For $50,000," Norma said.

"That is correct."

She made a scoffing sound. "That's crazy."

"Nonetheless, that is the proposition,"[2] Mr. Steward said. "Would you like me to return the button unit?"

Norma stiffened. *"Certainly not."* She hung up angrily.

▲ ▲ ▲

The package was lying by the front door; Norma saw it as she left the elevator. Well, of all the nerve, she thought. She glared at the carton as she unlocked the door. I just won't take it in, she thought. She went inside and started dinner.

Later, she went into the front hall. Opening the door, she picked up the package and carried it into the kitchen, leaving it on the table.

She sat in the living room, looking out the window. After a while, she went back into the kitchen to turn the cutlets[3] in the broiler. She put the package in a bottom cabinet. She'd throw it out in the morning.

▲ ▲ ▲

2 **proposition:** offer; proposal

3 **cutlets:** pieces of meat cut to serving size

"Maybe some eccentric millionaire is playing games with people," she said.

Arthur looked up from his dinner. "I don't understand you."

"What does *that* mean?"

"Let it go," he told her.

Norma ate in silence. Suddenly, she put her fork down. "Suppose it's a genuine offer?" she said.

Arthur stared at her.

"Suppose it's a genuine offer?"

"All right, suppose it is?" He looked incredulous.[4] "What would you like to do? Get the button back and push it? *Murder* someone?"

Norma looked disgusted. *"Murder."*

"How would you define it?"

"If you don't even *know* the person?" Norma said.

Arthur looked astounded. "Are you saying what I think you are?"

"If it's some old Chinese peasant ten thousand miles away? Some diseased native in the Congo?"

"How about a baby boy in Pennsylvania?" Arthur countered. "Some beautiful little girl on the next block?"

"Now you're loading things."

"The point is, Norma," he continued, "what's the difference whom you kill? It's still murder."

"The point *is,*" Norma broke in, "if it's someone you've never seen in your life and never *will* see, someone whose death you don't even have to *know* about, you *still* wouldn't push the button?"

Arthur stared at her, appalled. "You mean *you would?*"

"Fifty thousand dollars, Arthur."

"What has the amount—"

"Fifty thousand dollars, Arthur," Norma interrupted. "A chance to take that trip to Europe we've always talked about."

"Norma, no."

"A chance to buy that cottage on the island."

"Norma, *no.*" His face was white.

She shuddered. "All right, take it easy," she said. "Why are you getting so upset? It's only talk."

After dinner, Arthur went into the living room. Before he left the table, he said, "I'd rather not discuss it anymore, if you don't mind."

---

4 **incredulous:** doubtful; suspicious

Norma shrugged. "Fine with me."

▲   ▲   ▲

She got up earlier than usual to make pancakes, eggs, and bacon for Arthur's breakfast.

"What's the occasion?" he asked with a smile.

"No occasion." Norma looked offended. "I wanted to do it, that's all."

"Good," he said. "I'm glad you did."

She refilled his cup. "Wanted to show you I'm not—" She shrugged.

"Not what?"

"Selfish."

"Did I say you were?"

"Well"—she gestured vaguely—"last night . . ."

Arthur didn't speak.

"All that talk about the button," Norma said. "I think you—well, misunderstood me."

"In what way?" His voice was guarded.

"I think you felt"—she gestured again—"that I was only thinking of myself."

"Oh."

"I wasn't."

"Norma—"

"Well, I *wasn't*. When I talked about Europe, a cottage on the island—"

"Norma, why are we getting so involved in this?"

"I'm not involved at all." She drew in a shaking breath. "I'm simply trying to indicate that—"

"What?"

"That I'd like for *us* to go to Europe. Like for *us* to have a cottage on the island. Like for *us* to have a nicer apartment, nicer furniture, nicer clothes, a car. Like for us to finally have a *baby,* for that matter."

"Norma, we will," he said.

"When?"

He stared at her in dismay. "Norma—"

"When?!"

"Are you"—he seemed to draw back slightly—"are you really saying—"

"I'm saying that they're probably doing it for some research project!" she cut him off. "That they want to know what average people would do under such a circumstance! That they're just *saying* someone would die, in order to study reactions, see if there'd be guilt, anxiety, whatever! You don't think they'd *kill* somebody, do you?!"

Arthur didn't answer. She saw his hands trembling. After a while, he got up and left.

When he'd gone to work, Norma remained at the table, staring into her coffee. I'm going to be late, she thought. She shrugged. What difference did it make? She should be home, anyway, not working in an office.

▲ ▲ ▲

While she was stacking dishes, she turned abruptly, dried her hands, and took the package from the bottom cabinet. Opening it, she set the button unit on the table. She stared at it for a long time before taking the key from its envelope and removing the glass dome. She stared at the button. How ridiculous, she thought. All this furor over a meaningless button.

Reaching out, she pressed it down. For *us*, she thought angrily.

She shuddered. Was it *happening*? A chill of horror swept across her.

In a moment, it had passed. She made a contemptuous noise. *Ridiculous*, she thought. To get so worked up over nothing.

She threw the button unit, dome, and key into the wastebasket and hurried to dress for work.

▲ ▲ ▲

She had just turned over the supper steaks when the telephone rang. She picked up the receiver. "Hello?"

"Mrs. Lewis?"

"Yes?"

"This is the Lenox Hill Hospital."

She felt unreal as the voice informed her of the subway accident—the shoving crowd, Arthur pushed from the platform in front of the train. She was conscious of shaking her head but couldn't stop.

As she hung up, she remembered Arthur's life-insurance policy for $25,000, with double indemnity for—

"No." She couldn't seem to breathe. She struggled to her feet and walked into the kitchen numbly. Something cold pressed at her skull as she removed the button unit from the wastebasket. There were no nails or screws visible. She couldn't see how it was put together.

Abruptly, she began to smash it on the sink edge, pounding it harder and harder, until the wood split. She pulled the sides apart, cutting her fingers without noticing. There were no transistors in the box, no wires or tubes.

The box was empty.

She whirled with a gasp as the telephone rang. Stumbling into the living room, she picked up the receiver.

"Mrs. Lewis?" Mr. Steward asked.

It wasn't her voice shrieking so; it couldn't be. *"You said I wouldn't know the one that died!"*

"My dear lady," Mr. Steward said. "Do you really think you knew your husband?" ∾

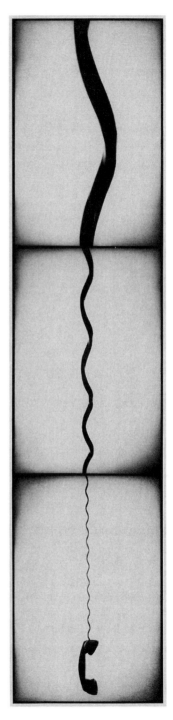

RESPONDING TO CLUSTER THREE

WHAT ARE THE POSSIBLE CONSEQUENCES OF OUR DECISIONS?

Thinking Skill PREDICTING

1. In "Ashes," Ashleigh has to decide if she will "borrow" $200 from her mother at her father's request. List the pros and cons of her choices; then **predict** which choice she will make. Finally, **predict** the consequences of each choice.

2. The diagram below shows the traditional structure of a story: beginning, rising action, turning point, falling action, and conclusion. Some nontraditional stories do not follow this pattern, however. Using a graphic such as the one below, show how the plot develops in "Button, Button" and "Ashes." Decide which of the stories is traditional and which is nontraditional. Which do you prefer?

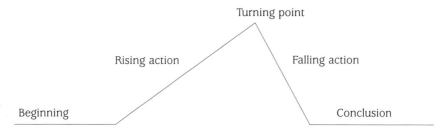

Turning point

Rising action

Falling action

Beginning

Conclusion

3. A **moral** is the point or lesson of a story. For example, the moral of the fable "The Tortoise and the Hare" could be "slow and steady wins the race." Stories often have more than one meaning and different readers may take different lessons from the same story. Write a moral for your favorite selection in this cluster.

4. Slade Anderson in "Moving into the Mainstream" decides to attend a school with both sighted and blind students. **Predict** how this decision might affect his future.

Writing Activity: The Rest of the Story

In several paragraphs, continue one of the stories you have read so far, focusing on possible consequences of a decision a character makes, or is about to make. For example, you might describe Ashleigh's thoughts as she makes her final choice, or you might show what becomes of Norma and the black box in "Button, Button."

To Move Beyond the Story

• take into account what has already happened

• consider the character and personalities of the people involved

• suggest a scenario that is logical within the context of the story

CLUSTER FOUR

Thinking on Your Own
Thinking Skill SYNTHESIZING

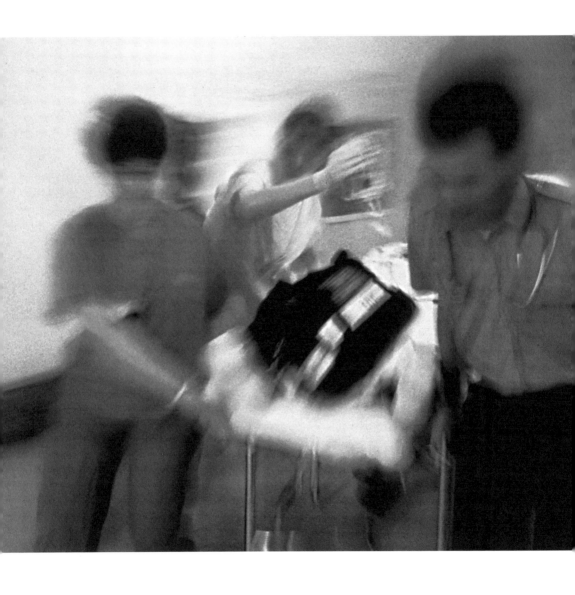

The Price of Life

PAMELA GRIM

*Medical doctor Pamela Grim is a
main character in the true story she tells here.*

John Simon was a business executive for a prominent health insurance company. During a seminar on health care management, he sneezed, then sagged out of his chair and slid to the floor. The first thing he saw was the face of the woman who'd sat beside him.

"What happened?" he asked, but he didn't recognize his voice or his words as he said them. He reached up, but as he did, his hand seemed to disappear. People gathered round. All of them were talking, but as if from far away. Someone kept saying, "911, 911, 911." Maybe he kept saying it. Faces disappeared and reappeared, but that one woman was always there. He tried to think. She had told him she was once a nurse; now she was a lawyer. She looked very much a nurse now, leaning over him. They had talked about contracts during lunch. What was her name? And he saw his wife momentarily next to her, which was strange because this was a business seminar. He couldn't remember his wife's name either.

Two men, young men in uniforms, came to take care of him. He thought they were policemen at first but then realized they were paramedics.[1] They got out their equipment and attached monitor leads and oxygen to him, which was ridiculous. Look at this: now they were trying to take his blood pressure.

"What is it?" he asked. "What's wrong with me?"

---

[1] **paramedics:** medical technicians who provide emergency services

"Sir, I think you're having a stroke."

"This is absurd," he thought. "I'm only 37." He tried to sit up but couldn't. He felt as if he were drowning.

They set off in the ambulance, careering[2] around corners, which he thought was funny; it wasn't as if he were dying. Then he realized it wasn't so funny. After a while the ambulance doors opened and he was rolled inside a hospital. People were trailing the gurney[3] as it rolled along. All were dressed in green scrubs, except one woman in a white lab coat. She had dark hair and a stethoscope slung around her neck. She must be the doctor, he thought. Women are doctors now, men are nurses, and nurses are lawyers. For a moment he was buoyant,[4] lifted up onto the bed by a sea of hands. Then that woman, the doctor, leaned over him and asked questions. What was his name? How old was he?

That doctor was me.

Quick check. Blood pressure 160/90, pulse 88, breathing unlabored. Spontaneous eye opening. "Sir, sir! What's his name? Mr. Simon, sir, I'm your doctor." Pupils are equal and reactive. Normal heart sounds. "Sir, squeeze my hand. Squeeze with your right hand. Good. Now squeeze with your left. Squeeze your left hand. . . ."

Nothing. This 37-year-old otherwise healthy male has had a sudden neurological event—probably a stroke.

The admitting clerk was there, pad and pencil in hand. "Sir, when's your birthday? Do you have your insurance card? Who's your doctor?" She stood there asking questions that are really irrelevant in the early care of a critically ill patient. But unfortunately, when someone suffers a stroke there's not much care to interfere with, beyond the physical exam itself. Other than giving oxygen, controlling blood pressure, and correcting incidental problems, a doctor can do little more than wait and see whether the stroke symptoms get better or worse. At least that's the way it's been. Now there may be a new treatment, and that, for me, was even more of a problem.

I had read glowing reports that a clot-busting drug used to treat heart attacks could be used to treat certain stroke patients, dramatically reducing their risk of a catastrophic deficit.[5] This would indeed be wonderful,

2 **careering:** going at top speed; traveling recklessly
3 **gurney:** a wheeled stretcher
4 **buoyant:** floating
5 **catastrophic deficit:** overwhelming loss; in this case, of body functions

but I was skeptical. I was aware of recent studies showing that in some cases clot-busting drugs could make a stroke worse. In fact, only one study had shown a clear benefit for clot-busting drugs—and even then only in patients who had been treated within three hours of the onset of symptoms. So I had doubts, and those doubts made me apprehensive about how to treat Mr. Simon.

A stroke is the brain's version of a heart attack. There are two main kinds. One is caused by a clot in a blood vessel of the brain. The other is caused when a brain blood vessel ruptures and blood leaks into brain tissue. Both disrupt the oxygen flow in the brain, often causing permanent brain damage. A clot-busting drug can be helpful only in strokes caused by clots. If the stroke is from a *bleed,* the drug may make the bleed much worse, turning a stroke from mild to catastrophic.

How can you tell if a stroke is from a bleed or a clot? By doing a CT scan, the radiographic test[6] that has revolutionized brain imaging. The biggest problem is time. In some institutions a brain CT scan can be obtained in 15 to 20 minutes. In others it may take up to two hours. But studies show that if the clot-busting drug is to work, it has to be given early. And many patients with strokes don't get to the hospital until their symptoms are hours old, too late to begin administering the drug. Mr. Simon was lucky. He arrived minutes after the onset of his symptoms. If anyone could be helped by the drug, it would be him—that is, if he had a clot.

▲　▲　▲

Mr. Simon's exam showed a left facial droop, complete paralysis of the left hand, and marked weakness of the left leg. As I was running the reflex hammer along the bottom of his foot, I looked up and saw two nurses wheeling a bed containing an elderly woman. I had ordered a CT scan on her an hour before. "Stop!" I called. "He goes first."

I rode shotgun on the cart, pushing the IV pole along with the nurses in the parade down to the scanner. I sat behind the CT technician watching images from the core of the brain crystallizing and dissolving on the screen. There were the lovely patterns of nature—the sulci, the cerebrum, the thalamus, the falx.[7] All of the structures I had sweated to memorize in school were now laid out effortlessly before me.

6　**radiographic test:** a test that results in an image produced on a sensitized film or plate, usually by X-rays

7　**sulci; cerebrum; thalamus; falx:** parts of the brain

It was a matter of moments. I could see that John Simon's CT scan was normal.

This, obviously, did not mean his brain was normal. Patients with strokes from clots typically have CT scans in which the abnormality appears only after several hours. Bleeds, however, usually show up right away. John Simon appeared to have had a stroke caused by a clot.

I left a message for the attending neurologist; I was sure he would advise me to give a clot-busting drug. But I was still worried that in this case we might make things worse. Time ticked by. At last Dr. Zimmer returned my call.

"Normal guy," I said. "No history of medical problems. He was at a conference and he sneezed. . . ."

"Sneezed?"

"Sneezed."

"Dissection."

"What?"

"I think he may have a dissection."

That made sense. A dissection is a tiny tear *within* the lining of the blood vessel; it can impair blood flow disastrously without causing bleeding outside the blood vessel. Dissections are rare, but the sneeze could have caused one by momentarily increasing the pressure in Mr. Simon's brain. Treating a dissection with a clot-busting drug might indeed do more harm than good.

"On the other hand," he added, "it *could* be a clot. The only way to tell for sure is to do an angiogram."

An angiogram is performed by injecting dye into a brain artery; the dye allows us to trace blood flow and actually *see* whether a clot or dissection exists. It is much more difficult to do than a CT scan, and since it is invasive, somewhat more dangerous. But my hospital didn't have the sophisticated facilities and experienced staff to do angiograms.

"Try University Hospital," Dr. Zimmer said. "The brain attack team."

University Hospital was one of two local medical centers that advertised the newest treatments for stroke.

I hung up, dialed University's paging operator, and asked to speak to the "brain attack team." A Dr. Dash came on the line right away. She took the case after I had spoken only a few sentences.

"We'll get the angiography suite set up now. Send him over—fast. Time is critical." She turned away from the phone, and I could hear her say, "Where's the helicopter?"

"It's out," I heard someone shout.

Our hospital has a critical-care transport team, Lifeline. It was my turn to lean over to our clerk.

"Lifeline?" I asked Mary.

"They're out," she said. "And there's only one truck today."

Hospital cutbacks.

She raised a finger, though. "Let me see what I can do."

"Doctor." Lynn, the head ER nurse, came up to the desk. "Why don't you come and take another look at this guy."

I ran to Mr. Simon's room. If anything, he looked worse. Now he couldn't move his left leg at all. I flicked my pen up the bottom of his foot and his toes fanned out, the big toe arching away from my pen. The "not a good sign" sign. He was losing more motor control.

His wife had arrived. I tried to explain to her what was happening, but she was nearly hysterical. "Please, doctor," she said, "please help him."

I said I wanted to transfer him to University Hospital. "They have a team of specialists that may be able to treat him with things we can't." Maybe, I told myself, maybe, maybe. "They can do an angiogram. . . ." I balked at trying to explain an angiogram to this frantic woman.

Someone tapped my arm. It was my patient nudging me with his right hand. Even that hand seemed weak now. He tried to speak but gave up; his speech was slurred. He raised his hand into a recognizable okay sign—"okay to transfer."

Mary, leaning into the room, announced that she had a transport team—a paramedic who knew how to drive the truck, and the head nurse, Lynn. It was now an hour and 35 minutes since Mr. Simon's collapse. I could only pray for an uneventful ambulance ride and a quick response on the other side.

Just as they were heading out of the room, there was a phone call for me.

"It's Dr. Dash," Mary told me.

I grabbed the phone. "We're just loading him," I said. "He'll be there shortly."

"No, you have to stop."

"Stop? Why?"

"Our clinical coordinator contacted your registration clerk. You can't transfer him here. This man has the wrong insurance."

"What?"

"The wrong insurance. You never checked his insurance status. We don't take his insurance. You never checked."

"That's the last thing in the world I'm worried about."

"Look. Take him to the Foundation Hospital. They have a brain attack team, and I think they're accepting patients."

"But that will put us another hour behind. Look, you accepted him, and you've got everything set up." I was furious, helplessly watching all the time we saved go down the drain. "The Foundation Hospital may not even accept him."

"They'll accept him," she said. "I'm pretty sure."

"But I just told him and his wife that University Hospital is the best place in the city for strokes. Now you want me to tell them I'm sending him to the *other* best place in the city for strokes."

"Is his wife there? I'll explain it."

The team came wheeling out into the hallway, the patient in a tangle of wires from the portable monitors, oxygen tubing, and IV lines. "*Stop!*" I shouted, hands up in the air.

"What's going on?" Lynn asked. Everyone floundered to a halt and looked at me. "What? What?"

I waved the wife over. She looked even worse than the patient, if that was possible. I handed her the phone receiver and told her to talk to the doctor. I went over to Lynn. "He's got the wrong insurance," I whispered. "They want us to send him to the Foundation Hospital."

We looked at each other, stunned.

I looked over at the wife. Her hand was drooping so that the receiver was nowhere near her ear. She was clearly in no shape to make a decision. I stood there for a moment thinking, "This cannot be real." Then I ran over to her and grabbed the phone away.

"We've wasted precious time already. You've accepted him. He's coming to you! End of discussion."

Dr. Dash sounded almost relieved. "Okay, okay. Send him here. We'll deal with all that later."

I slammed down the phone and waved to Lynn. "University!" I shouted, and they were off.

I sat down and stared at my hands. In medicine we have grown so accustomed to the splendid luxury of cost being no object that any financial restraint seems intrusive. This financial concern, however, was more like appalling.

I sat there with my head in my hands.

It occurred to me that I might be liable for the cost of this man's stay.

After all, I had just knowingly sent him to a hospital not covered by his insurance. I never obtained his permission. Maybe I would have to pay the bill. Then I shook myself. We all, the nurses and the techs and I, had gotten this patient seen, scanned, and transferred in about an hour. If this man had any chance to recover, it would be because of this. We did what was best for him.

I thought about what strokes of this magnitude can mean: paralysis, feeding tubes, indwelling urine catheters,[8] bedsores[9] so erosive they take on a life of their own. You can't walk without assistance; you can't bathe; you can't dress. You can't sing; you can't dance.

But you can still cry.

An hour later Dr. Dash called me. There was something wrong with her voice. It took me a moment to realize she was crying.

"What *happened?*" I shouted. "Was it a dissection or a clot or what?"

"He had a clot," she sobbed back. "A big clot right in the middle cerebral artery.[10] We went in. You could see it beautifully on the screen. We gave him the drug and the clot just vanished. His leg strength has completely returned, and he's moving his arm much better. Nearly full recovery!"

I felt for a moment how a saint must feel when attendant at a miracle, simultaneously very big and very small.

"He wants to go home," Dr. Dash said. "He wants to go back to his business conference. He wants to know why he is here."

"Tell him. . . ." I started to say but stopped. I was going to say, "Tell him he's there because I sent him to the *wrong* hospital to get a medication that I didn't think would work."

I hung up the phone and covered my face with my hands. There I was, humbled again. This, I thought, must be the "art" of medicine. ∾

---

8 **indwelling urine catheters:** tubes inserted in the body to drain urine

9 **bedsores:** deep sores on the skin caused by the pressure of the body on the bed when a patient is bedridden

10 **cerebral artery:** a blood vessel in the brain

i'll never

TODD MOORE

i'll never
understand why
thompson didn't
shoot that big
timber wolf down
by dead prophet
creek he had it
nailed to the
crosshairs of
his sniper's
scope i cd feel
that greasy rifle
steel lean into
my finger & wanted
to swim inside
the embrace of
man & gun but he
wdn't fire when
he used the rifle
to look away i
knew it was
over except for
the sound of
wind in the
grass then he
levered the
shell & gave it
to me didn't you
hear it he asked
hear what
thompson smiled
the wolf was
singing

Above: Rosa Parks in a recreated photo taken in 1956, one year after the famous bus ride.
Left: Rosa Parks, 1999.

The Front of the Bus

ROSA PARKS

December 1, 1955
Montgomery, Alabama

"I don't think any segregation law angered black people in Montgomery more than bus segregation," Rosa Parks recalled years after this incident, which sparked the Montgomery bus boycott. The two-thirds of the city bus riders who were African Americans were forced to endure humiliating rules, including a requirement that they sit in the back of the bus. Bus drivers, who carried guns, had police power to enforce the regulations. When a local NAACP[1] official requested a change in one of the rules, he was told, "Your folks started it. They do it because they want to."

Parks was secretary of the local chapter of the NAACP at the time. She has often been described as merely a seamstress who was too tired to move. That poignant version belies the college-educated Parks's long history as a knowledgeable, committed activist. It also ignores the stand she had taken twelve years earlier, in 1943, when a bus driver told her to move to the back. She refused, and the driver forced her off the bus. After avoiding that driver for more than a decade, she found herself on his bus once again. This time she was prepared to see the confrontation through to its end.

The boycott lasted more than a year. The bus company lost two-thirds of its income, and caved in. The action also brought national attention to its leader, Dr. Martin Luther King, Jr.

---

1 **NAACP:** National Association for the Advancement of Colored People

In December 1956, the U.S. Supreme Court ruled that bus segregation is illegal. The bus driver who forced Parks off the bus in 1943 and 1955 remained in his job until 1972, when he retired.

When I got off from work that evening of December 1, I went to Court Square as usual to catch the Cleveland Avenue bus home. I didn't look to see who was driving when I got on, and by the time I recognized him, I had already paid my fare. It was the same driver who had put me off the bus back in 1943, twelve years earlier. He was still tall and heavy, with red, rough-looking skin. And he was still mean-looking. I didn't know if he had been on that route before—they switched the drivers around sometimes. I do know that most of the time if I saw him on a bus, I wouldn't get on it.

I saw a vacant seat in the middle section of the bus and took it. I didn't even question why there was a vacant seat even though there were quite a few people standing in the back. If I had thought about it at all, I would probably have figured maybe someone saw me get on and did not take the seat but left it vacant for me. There was a man sitting next to the window and two women across the aisle.

The next stop was the Empire Theater, and some whites got on. They filled up the white seats, and one man was left standing. The driver looked back and noticed the man standing. Then he looked back at us. He said, "Let me have those front seats," because they were the front seats of the black section. Didn't anybody move. We just sat right where we were, the four of us. Then he spoke a second time: "Y'all better make it light on yourselves and let me have those seats."

The man in the window seat next to me stood up, and I moved to let him pass by me, and then I looked across the aisle and saw that the two women were also standing. I moved over to the window seat. I could not see how standing up was going to "make it light" for me. The more we gave in and complied, the worse they treated us.

I thought back to the time when I used to sit up all night and didn't sleep, and my grandfather would have his gun right by the fireplace, or if he had his one-horse wagon going anywhere, he always had his gun in the back of the wagon. People always say that I didn't give up my seat because I was tired, but that isn't true. I was not tired physically, or no more tired than I usually was at the end of a working day. I was not old, although some people have an image of me as being old then. I was forty-two. No, the only tired I was, was tired of giving in.

The driver of the bus saw me still sitting there, and he asked was I going to stand up. I said, "No." He said, "Well, I'm going to have you arrested." Then I said, "You may do that." These were the only words we said to each other. I didn't even know his name, which was James Blake, until we were in court together. He got out of the bus and stayed outside for a few minutes, waiting for the police.

As I sat there, I tried not to think about what might happen. I knew that anything was possible. I could be manhandled or beaten. I could be arrested. People have asked me if it occurred to me then that I could be the test case the NAACP had been looking for. I did not think about that at all. In fact if I had let myself think too deeply about what might happen to me, I might have gotten off the bus. But I chose to remain.

Meanwhile there were people getting off the bus and asking for transfers, so that began to loosen up the crowd, especially in the back of the bus. Not everyone got off, but everybody was very quiet. What conversation there was, was in low tones; no one was talking out loud. It would have been quite interesting to have seen the whole bus empty out. Or if the other three had stayed where they were, because if they'd had to arrest four of us instead of one, then that would have given me a little support. But it didn't matter. I never thought hard of them at all and never even bothered to criticize them.

Eventually two policemen came. They got on the bus, and one of them asked me why I didn't stand up. I asked him, "Why do you all push us around?" He said to me, and I quote him exactly, "I don't know, but the law is the law and you're under arrest." ॐ

The Order of Things

MICHEL FOUCAULT

People know what they do;
they frequently know why they do what they do;
but what they don't know
is what what they do does.

Gifted

DAVE BARRY

When I was a small boy, gift shopping was simple, because I had very few people to buy gifts for, and once I found a gift that worked, I stuck with it, year after year. For example, I always gave my father a belt. I got it at the five-and-ten-cent store for about a dollar. It was made from what appeared to be genuine hand-tooled cardboard. I doubt that my father ever wore any of these belts, because if the humidity got over 50 percent they would dissolve. But it never occurred to me to wonder whether my father needed a belt; all I knew was that belts were in my price range, and he always said thank you.

I always gave my mother a little bottle of toilet water, which also cost about a dollar. At first I believed that this was water from an actual *toilet*, and I had no idea what she was supposed to do with it. But it came in a nice bottle, and it was also in my price range, and my mother always acted thrilled, holding the bottle up for general admiration.

"Look what Davey got me!" she'd exclaim, in a voice containing no hint of the fact that this was the fourth consecutive Christmas she'd received it. "Toilet water!"

I usually made Christmas gifts for my sister. One year I made her a paperweight by getting some clay and letting it harden, thereby forming a hardened lump of clay.

"What is this?" she asked.

"A paperweight," I said.

"Thank you," she said, which I now realize was very gracious of her. It was not as if the lack of a good paperweight had left a gaping hole in her life.

Another year I made her a bookmark. It looked very much like an ordinary strip of construction paper, but the trained eye could tell it was a bookmark, because on it were written, in crayon, the words BOOK MARK. I am sure she couldn't wait to finish opening her other presents so she could race to her room and mark some books.

The point is, gift-giving was simple for me then. As you have no doubt noticed, the older you get, and the more obligations you develop, the more complex the gift-giving becomes. This is especially true if you have children on your gift list. Meeting the gift needs of a single modern child requires an effort of roughly the same magnitude as the Normandy Invasion.[1]

You parents know what I'm talking about. You know what it means to race from store to store, looking desperately for the Number-One Item on your eight-year-old son's wish list, namely the Official NASA Model Junior Space Shuttle, which takes seventeen years to assemble and leaks real hydrogen. You know what it means to get into a semiviolent dispute with another parent over who gets to purchase the only remaining model of the heavily advertised hot new toy concept Baby Fester Face ("The Doll with Open Sores That Really Run!"), which your five-year-old daughter has informed you she absolutely MUST have this year, and if she doesn't get it, she's going to put her own self up for adoption.

But at least children know what they want. It's much harder to decide what to get for grown-ups, who almost never know what they want, which is why we generally wind up giving them stupid things. For example, men are always getting cologne. I have never, in my whole life, heard a man express even the slightest interest in cologne. But most of us have numerous bottles of it, dating back to the Johnson administration.[2]

What do men *really* want? I am generalizing here, of course, but I'd say that what men really want is to be left alone at key moments. For example, if you're in a relationship with a man, and you have decided, after much thought, that the two of you need to have a long, probing conversation in which you both sincerely try to understand each other's innermost feelings, then the man would consider it a wonderful gift if you would NOT announce your decision during an important televised football game (defined as "any televised football game").

Another great gift for a guy would be to tell him that you took the car in and had the oil changed AND the tires rotated.

1 **Normandy Invasion:** a major World War II battle

2 **Johnson administration:** the administration of American President Lyndon B. Johnson, 1963–69

But usually what we get is cologne.

What women really want, of course, is for men to share their innermost feelings. So what most men give them is appliances. I was guilty of this for many years, until I realized that although my wife could *appreciate* a fine appliance, she couldn't really *cherish* it. You never see scenes like this in the movies:

BRAD: Well, Dorothy, I'm off to the war.

DOROTHY: Oh, Brad, please be careful!

BRAD: I shall, Dorothy. But just in case I don't come back, I want you to have this.

DOROTHY: (*tears of happiness streaming down her face:*) Oh, Brad! It's a General Electric

Coffee Maker with 12-Cup Capacity *and* Auto-Timer Function!

I have gradually learned that, as a rule, women prefer romantic items, which can be defined as "items that are small but cost a lot and do not have plugs," such as jewelry. The ultimate romantic gift for a woman would be a *single molecule* of some extremely expensive substance in a tiny cherishable box.

But you'll probably get her a Water Pik, you dork. ∾

The Dandelion Garden

A Modern Fable for Elderly Children

BUDGE WILSON

In a land not far away and not so long ago, a son was born to two people of humble means. Although low in funds, the father was high in pretensions, and named his son Hamlet.[1] "For," he explained, "this is no ordinary boy. He is our firstborn, and I intend that he shall be profound and inscrutable[2] and undeniably great."

Hamlet displayed a notable lack of profundity[3] during the first five years of his life. He did all the usual things. This pleased his father, who, like all parents, regarded usual things as unusual when performed by his own child. He developed remarkable and miraculous skills: he learned how to unbutton his shoes, to go to the bathroom, to throw a ball, to catch beetles, and to color between the lines. "Clearly," said the father, as he watched this singular development from nothing to something, "this is no ordinary child."

Then, in the spring of one memorable year, Hamlet had his fifth birthday. On the day after his birthday, when he was just five years and twenty-four hours old, he took a spade into the garden, with the intention of increasing his collection of beetles. Upon entering the garden, however, he stopped short, with one of his legs suspended two inches from the ground. He dropped his spade, as the delight of his discovery

---

1 **Hamlet:** the main character in Shakespeare's play, *Hamlet*
2 **inscrutable:** unknowable; unexplainable
3 **profundity:** wisdom; depth

drained the strength from his arms. He sat down so that he might survey the miracle at closer range. The lawn was a lawn no longer. It was a sea of sunshine, and the flowers that made up the infinity of yellowness were everywhere. When he recovered from the initial shock, Hamlet snatched one of the flowers from its stem and rushed into the house.

"What is it?" he demanded of his mother, thrusting the flower before her eyes.

"A dandelion, of course," said his mother, looking at the flower with distaste.

He hardly dared ask the next question. At last he summoned the courage. "Is it strong?" he asked nervously. "Will it grow easily?"

His mother searched about in her mind for an adjective capable of describing the gargantuan[4] strength of dandelions. Finally she resorted to the force of simplicity and gave her answer. *"Very,"* she replied.

The boy's relief was enormous. For a moment it was enough to know that the flowers would endure and come again. But soon the desire to possess the object of his love overcame him. "Could I," he faltered. "May I . . . *take* some?"

"Please, do," said his mother with feeling, and disappeared upstairs to make the beds.

Beetles were forgotten. So also were balls, swings, crayons, and Sunday-school picnics. He applied himself with concentration and devotion and toil and delicacy to the planting of a dandelion garden. He chose a spot at the back of the yard behind the hedge, where he might work unnoticed and undisturbed. "I'm making a surprise, I'm making a surprise," he chanted over and over to himself, as he thrust his spade into the earth; then he made up a little tune to go with the words. He dug up the plants one by one from the lawn, removing each one with such care that not a leaf was harmed. This took a long time. Next he made a soft roomy hole, deposited the plant, sprinkled it with fertilizer, and watered it carefully, generously, and accurately. Then he patted it lovingly into the ground. By the end of two weeks, he had forty-two plants in his garden. He was satisfied. The display was adequate in numbers and very splendid in effect. It was five o'clock, and he was tired.

He chose his mother first. He chose her because he loved her, and also because there was no one else around at the time. He dashed, he tore, he flew into the kitchen, and, pulling at his mother's apron, gasped,

---

4 **gargantuan:** huge

"Come! Come! Come quickly to the garden and see my surprise!"

Hamlet's mother paused for a moment in the middle of her preparations for the evening meal. She looked at him and failed to notice the visionary glitter in his eyes. "Your face," she said, "is dirty. Go wash and tidy yourself before going any further."

Washed and combed, he returned, still aglow. "Come with me," he begged. "Come. Please. To the garden."

"Not now," she said, puncturing the balloon of his delight. "I have no time. I must peel the potatoes, heat the water, scrape the carrots, pour the milk, set the table, whip the cream, cook the meat, sweep the floor, and change my clothes before dinner. Tomorrow I will come. Not now. I have not time."

Hamlet shivered. But he answered, because he had no choice, "Yes, Mother, we will go tomorrow."

The next day, the dandelions were wilted and bent. Even dandelions will not last indefinitely, and their season was past. "Next year," said the boy, "is forever. But I will wait and build another garden in another spring, and this time I will take my father to see it. He will come."

The year passed, another spring arrived, and Hamlet was six. At the first appearance of dandelions, he started to work with great haste. This time he planted his garden with even more care, arranging the flowers in special groups, curves, and circles. It took him two weeks to complete it, and when it was done he stood back and surveyed it with joy and with pride.

He had learned something the previous year. He washed his hands and face carefully, and waited for the right moment to approach his father. When his father seemed comfortably occupied in doing nothing at all, Hamlet walked quickly up to him.

"Father," he began. "Father, please come with me. I have a surprise to show you—a fine thing I have made all by myself. It has taken me two weeks to finish it." He pulled at his father's arm.

"Fine, my son," said his father, already guessing at the nature of the surprise. It would be a tree house, a handmade steam engine, or a car fashioned from orange crates. Truly, Hamlet was a remarkably creative child. He followed his son into the backyard.

Hamlet was overwhelmed by his father's willingness to come. He could bear the suspense no longer. "Father," he cried, "my surprise is a dandelion garden!"

His father stopped walking. "A garden?" he thought, with deep dismay.

"My son, my firstborn—a wimp!" He turned to his son in anger, and then checked himself. "This is a problem of great delicacy," he argued to himself. "As a wise father, I will handle it with control and with calm." Thus he congratulated himself.

"Let us have a little talk, first," said his father, placing a hand upon Hamlet's shoulder. Despite the warmth of the afternoon, Hamlet could feel a chilly wind on the back of his neck. "All right, Father," he replied, his eyes fastened upon the hedge.

"Boys," said the father, "are different from girls. They like climbing trees and building boats and throwing balls and playing marbles and going fishing and making forts and having snowball fights. Boys are not interested in flowers. Sometimes men plant gardens, but this is in order to improve the value of their property. Your mother is calling us in to dinner." Then his father, in a generous welling-up of understanding and wisdom, once more placed his hand upon Hamlet's shoulder. "I'm sure," he concluded, "that we understand one another."

That evening Hamlet looked lovingly at his garden. He already possessed it, but now the desire to share it with someone else was a flood straining to be loosed. Tomorrow he would find that person.

But the next day was the fifteenth day, and it was too late. The garden was no longer in full bloom, and there is nothing sadder than a withered flower. "Next year," sighed Hamlet, "is forever and ever, but I will make another garden and show it to a gardener. A gardener is a lover of flowers and will understand."

The leaves fell and the snow passed, and it was spring again. In greatest secrecy, Hamlet planted his garden, more intricate and magnificent than ever before. On the fourteenth day, he gazed upon the blooms and knew that this was more beautiful than the other gardens. The dandelions were tall and strong; their blooms were like the rays of the sun; the design of their arrangement was marvelous to see. He went forth in search of a gardener.

"Gardener," he said when he finally found one, "I have made a garden. Will you come to see it?"

"Good," exclaimed the gardener. "I would like very much to see your garden. No doubt the flowers are very beautiful. I trust that you have eliminated all the weeds."

"What is a weed?" asked Hamlet.

"A weed," said the gardener, "is a very terrible thing, and the worst kind of weed is a dandelion. It tries hard to grow in every flower garden.

It even invades the lawns. Everyone knows that each blade of grass must be rescued from the ravages of a dandelion. I have in my pocket a very effective weed-killer. Since you are interested in gardens, you may have this bottle. Sprinkle a little on every dandelion tonight, and by morning each one will be twisted and wilted and completely dead. Now—take me to see your garden."

The gardener looked around in surprise. The boy was gone. He shrugged his shoulders and returned to his job of grafting[5] two rare rose-bushes.

It was six o'clock now, and too late for Hamlet to find someone else before the dawning of the fifteenth day. He spent the evening watering his garden. He wore a heavy sweater, because he felt very cold.

And so it came to pass that each year Hamlet spent two weeks making a dandelion garden. Every year it was finer than it had been the year before. On the fourteenth day he always looked for one person with whom he could share it.

One year he asked a schoolteacher to come and admire his blooms. "How long has it taken you to tend this garden?" she asked.

"Two weeks," he replied.

"And how much time have you spent on arithmetic and spelling and history and geography and grammar?" she inquired.

"Not much time at all," he answered. "But a dandelion is a wonderful thing. You can lick the end of it and make the stem curl into a hundred different curves and wiggles."

"That," she said, "is of no educational value, and is therefore of no significance."

He spoke one spring to a businessman of great wealth and prominence. "This is an idle way to spend your time, my boy," said the man. "You must apply yourself to life in a practical way, collecting enough knowledge and skill to make yourself wealthy and important."

"But," argued Hamlet, "a dandelion is a very useful thing. When it has gone to seed you can blow the seeds away and find out what time it is."

"Ah," sighed the man, "but you may blow the wrong number of times, and therefore be confused as to the correct time. To a man of business, the correct time is of prime importance. The reason you give for valuing a dandelion is of no significance at all."

---

5 **grafting:** inserting a shoot or stem of one plant into the stem of another so that they grow together

A clergyman admonished him for spending his time in a useless way, asking if he had done any good works or said any prayers during the two-week interval. Hamlet could recall neither good works nor prayers. However, he replied, "Dandelions can be used for good purposes. You can poke holes in their stems, put other dandelions in the holes, weave them together, and make a flower chain. This can be presented as a gift to one's grandmother, to place about her neck."

"This is a very frivolous purpose," replied the clergyman, "and cannot be regarded as of any significance."

Finally he found an artist. "Surely," he felt, "she will come to my garden and will marvel at its great beauty."

"Most flowers are lovely," she told him, "but if there is any flower that can be regarded as commonplace, it is the dandelion. Why do you not plant roses?"

"But the dandelion is the first flower of the year," he replied," and it is also of a perfect symmetrical form."

"It matters not at all if a flower arrives in May or December," she argued, "and besides, a dandelion is too perfect. Were I to paint a field of dandelions, I could put dabs of yellow paint at random throughout the grass on my picture, and everyone would say, 'Yes, those are dandelions.' But were I to paint a rose, I would have to paint each petal with infinite care."

Hamlet did not bother to reply. Her arguments, he felt, were of no significance at all. Besides, he was tired. He was tired of arguing, tired of searching, tired of planting. He was, in fact, tired of being young. He was eleven years old that spring.

The next year an old man came wandering through the land. No one knew where he came from or where he was going, but he seemed to be looking for someone. Finally he reached the town in which Hamlet lived. It was the fifteenth day of the garden, and Hamlet was sitting by the hedge, building a steam engine out of soup cans.

"I have been looking for you," said the man. "I am a dandelion grower. I am a hundred and ninety-nine years old and I have spent my life in the cultivation and care of dandelions. I have twenty-two acres of land on which are planted eighty-eight million dandelions. Every year I go on a long journey, searching for one other person with whom I can share my flowers. You are the person."

With listless eye, Hamlet looked up at the man. "It is too late," he replied. "I used to be a grower of dandelions myself, but now I am a

builder of steam engines. I am twelve years old, and I now know that the cultivation of dandelions is an unmanly pursuit. Dandelions are useless, time-consuming, frivolous, and much too common. Besides, they are weeds. Last night I, too, returned from my search for a person with whom to share my garden. Finding myself unsuccessful for the eighth time, I came back home and in great wrath stamped upon my flowers until they were all dead. I am twelve years old now, and very wise, and a maker of steam engines." The boy looked at him with such fierce determination that the old man knew it was useless to argue. He turned away from Hamlet and wept.

So Hamlet grew up to be a very efficient and successful engineer. By developing a habit of averting[6] his eyes when in the presence of dandelions, he became moderately content; indeed, in the course of time, he grew to be quite fond of engines and machines and bridges and dams. His father, of course, was both relieved and delighted by this turn of events. Nobody knows what became of the old man. There were not even any rumors, because no one was very interested. However, you may have noticed that dandelions are, if anything, on the increase. This fact may be of some significance.

On the other hand, it may mean nothing at all. ∿

---

6 **averting:** turning away

Obstacles

VIKTOR E. FRANKL

We who lived in the concentration camps can remember the men who walked through the huts comforting others, giving away their last piece of bread. They may have been few in number, but they offer sufficient proof that everything can be taken from a man but one thing: The last of his freedoms—to choose one's attitude in any given set of circumstances, to choose one's own way.

RESPONDING TO CLUSTER FOUR

Thinking Skill SYNTHESIZING

1. Each of the other clusters in this book is introduced by a question that is meant to help readers focus their thinking about the selections. What do you think the question for cluster four should be?

2. How do you think the selections in this cluster should be taught? Demonstrate your ideas by joining with your classmates to do one of more of the following:
   a. create discussion questions
   b. lead discussions about the selections
   c. develop vocabulary activities
   d. prepare a cluster quiz

REFLECTING ON *DECISIONS, DECISIONS*

Essential Question HOW DO I MAKE A DECISION?

Reflecting on this book as a whole provides an opportunity for independent learning and the application of the critical thinking skill, synthesis. *Synthesizing* means examining all the things you have learned from this book and combining them to form a richer and more meaningful view of how we learn to make decisions.

There are many ways to demonstrate what you know about making decisions. Here are some possibilities. Your teacher may provide others.

1. Describe a decision, such as choosing a career, that you will need to make in the next few years. List the factors you will need to consider before making that decision. Then predict what your decision will be. You might want to show your decision-making process in an essay, chart, poem, or artistic rendering.

2. Individually or with a small group, research what steps were followed in making important world, national, or local decisions such as the dropping of the atomic bomb, the building of the Alaska pipeline, or the return of the Panama Canal to the Panamanians. Present the pros and cons of the issue in a speech, essay, or debate. Then explain why you think the people involved made a good or bad decision.

3. Choose your favorite or least favorite story in this book. Tell the reasons why you would or would not have chosen to include it in this anthology.

Acknowledgments

Text Credits CONTINUED FROM PAGE 2

From *Dave Barry's Gift Guide to End All Gift Guides* by Dave Barry. Copyright © 1994 by Dave Barry. Reprinted by permission of Crown Publishers, a division of Random House, Inc.

"Dusting" from *Homecoming* by Julia Alvarez. Copyright © 1984, 1996 by Julia Alvarez. Published by Plume, an imprint of Dutton Signet, a division of Penguin USA; originally published by Grove Press. Reprinted by permission of Susan Bergholz Literary Services, New York. All rights reserved.

"Facing Donegall Square" from *Dancing Pink Flamingos and Other Stories* by Maria Testa. Copyright © 1995 by Lerner Publications. Used by permission of the publisher. All rights reserved.

"A Kind of Murder" by Hugh Pentecost. First published in *Ellery Queen's Mystery Magazine*. Copyright © 1962 by Hugh Pentecost. Copyright renewed © 1990 by Norma Phillips. Reprinted by permission of Brandt & Brandt Literary Agents, Inc.

"Long Walk To Forever," from *Welcome to the Monkey House* by Kurt Vonnegut, Jr. Copyright © 1961 by Kurt Vonnegut, Jr. Used by permission of Delacorte Press/Seymour Lawrence, a division of Random House, Inc.

From *Man's Search For Meaning* by Viktor E. Frankl. Copyright © 1959, 1962, 1984, 1992 by Viktor E. Frankl. Reprinted by permission of Beacon Press, Boston.

"Moving Into the Mainstream" by Slade Anderson from *Starting with "I": Personal Essays by Teenagers*, Andrea Estepa and Philip Kay, eds. Copyright © 1997 by Youth Communications®/New York Center, Inc. Reprinted by permission of Persea Books, Inc. (New York)

"The One Who Watches" from *An Island Like You: Stories of the Barrio* by Judith Ortíz Cofer. Copyright © 1994 by Judith Ortíz Cofer. Reprinted by permission of the publisher, Orchard Books, New York.

"Playing God," copyright © 1987 by Ouida Sebestyen, from *Visions* by Donald R. Gallo, editor. Used by permission of Dell Publishing, a division of Random House, Inc.

"The Price of Life" by Pamela Grim, *Discover*, September 1997. Copyright © 1997. Reprinted with permission of Discover Magazine.

From *Rosa Parks: My Story* by Rosa Parks with Jim Haskins, copyright © 1992 by Rosa Parks. Used by permission of Dial Books for Young Readers, a division of Penguin Putnam, Inc.

"TLA" by Jane McFann, from *Short Circuits*, edited by Donald R. Gallo (Delacorte). Copyright © 1992 by Jane McFann. Reprinted by permission of the author.

"Trapped in the Desert" by Gary Beeman. Reprinted with permission from the August 1964 *Reader's Digest*. Copyright © 1964 by The Reader's Digest Assn., Inc.

"Traveling Through the Dark" by William Stafford. Copyright © 1962, 1998 by the Estate of William Stafford. Reprinted from *The Way It Is: New & Selected Poems* with the permission of Graywolf Press, Saint Paul, Minnesota.

Every reasonable effort has been made to properly acknowledge ownership of all material used. Any omissions or mistakes are not intentional and, if brought to the publisher's attention, will be corrected in future editions.